INVESTIGATIONS
IN MATHEMATICS

INVESTIGATIONS IN MATHEMATICS

Lorraine Mottershead

Basil Blackwell

First published 1985

Published by
Basil Blackwell Limited
108 Cowley Road
Oxford OX4 1JF

Cover design by Indent, Reading
Typeset in Great Britain

Printed in Great Britain by The Pitman Press Ltd, Bath

British Library Cataloguing in Publication Data

Mottershead, Lorraine
    Investigations in mathematics.
    1. Mathematical recreations   2. Puzzles
    I. Title
    793.7'4   QA95

ISBN 0 631 90980 X

CONTENTS

INTRODUCTION

With the broadening of horizons in mathematics, teachers and students need to develop experimental and individual approaches, integrating enrichment topics with the fundamentals.

In searching for a broad definition of mathematics, I eventually decided on a simple yet effective phrase : *the study of patterns*. The topics in this book set out to show, in many ways, how this is what mathematics is. A multitude of number patterns, geometrical designs, block varieties, the geometry of flags, and numerous suggestions for making cardboard models, have been included. The final unit on great mathematicians is a brief summary of the life, times and investigations of a number of well-known people who have contributed greatly to the development of mathematics.

Topics are varied. My aim is to show how everyday things, that so many people take for granted (and therefore overlook), can be a valuable source of mathematics. As in *Sources of Mathematical Discovery*, these topics are only a starting point for teachers. Many could be used for research and lectures.

Practical activities should be an integral part of today's lessons. A large section in Unit 4 deals with numerous experiments suitable for any student. A wealth of clear illustrations should make it easy to adapt small sections to suit the needs of a class. Selected answers are given; the appropriate questions are indicated by *.

Investigations In Mathematics is a source book designed to provide effective practice in some basic concepts and skills in a form that generates interest and enthusiasm. This, hopefully, will lead the way to further investigations and experimentation. Students should derive pleasure from doing these topics and will appreciate, even more, the beauty and diversity as well as universality of mathematics.

Finally, I would like to express special thanks to all my students and colleagues, and especially to my family, for the inspiration, encouragement and patience shown to me while this book was being compiled.

L.J. Mottershead
1984

UNIT 1

IN SEARCH OF PATTERNS

Mathematics is the study of patterns. In this unit we shall look at the patterns, generated from number relationships, formed when elements are reduced to their digital sums. Often the term reduced number is used and indicates the single digit obtained by continued addition of the integers.

For example, if the digits of 14 are added $(1 + 4)$, the reduced number is 5.

Other examples :
$$324 \rightarrow 3 + 2 + 4 \qquad\qquad 226 \rightarrow 2 + 2 + 6$$
$$= 9 \qquad\qquad\qquad\qquad = 10$$
$$\rightarrow 1 + 0$$
$$= 1$$

The number of steps in the exercise is called its persistence number. In 21315, the persistence number is 2 because $21315 \rightarrow 12 \rightarrow 3$. Find the persistence number of a selection of numbers.

Reduced numbers form repeating cycles called periods, some being as large as 24.

Smaller periods are obtained by finding the reduced numbers of the multiplication tables. Look carefully at the following:

			Product	Reduced Number	
2 ×	1	=	2	2	P
2 ×	2	=	4	4	E
2 ×	3	=	6	6	R
2 ×	4	=	8	8	I
					O
2 ×	5	=	10	1	D
2 ×	6	=	12	3	
2 ×	7	=	14	5	O
2 ×	8	=	16	7	F
2 ×	9	=	18	9	
					9
2 × 10		=	20	2	
2 × 11		=	22	4	
2 × 12		=	24	6	
2 × 13		=	26	8	

The last digits in the *Product* column also form a repetitive sequence {2, 4, 6, 8, 0}. What would you expect the next set of reduced numbers to be?

1

When shown on a clockface, with digits 1 – 9 inclusive, this pattern emerges:

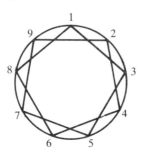

The three-times table has a much shorter set of repeating reduced numbers. Write them out in a similar way to the above. Find the period.
How are the elements connected?

The four-times table gives a more interesting set of results.

			Product	Reduced Numbers
4.× 1	=		4	4
4 × 2	=		8	8
4 × 3	=		12	3
4 × 4	=		16	7
4 × 5	=		20	2
4 × 6	=		24	6
4 × 7	=		28	1

The period of 9 is $\{5,9,4,8,3,7,2,6,1\}$ which is equivalent to the remainders when the product is divided by 9.
By arranging the digits into two alternating columns two distinct patterns are formed:

			Product	Reduced Numbers			
4 × 8	=		32	5		5	
4 × 9	=		36	9			9
4 ×10	=		40	4		4	
4 ×11	=		44	8			8
4 ×12	=		48	3		3	
4 ×13	=		52	7			7
4 ×14	=		56	2		2	
4 ×15	=		60	6			6
4 ×16	=		64	1		1	

On the clockface:

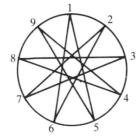

The five-times table is similar to the four-times. Write it out in full to see what the difference is. Go as far as 5×18. Alternate the reduced numbers. The clockface pattern should be the same, although it is done in reverse.

With the six-times table, the reduced numbers are similar to those of the three-times. Investigate. What is the length of the period?

There is a close connection between the seven-times and the two-times. Compare your results.

$\{8, 7, 6, 5, 4, 3, 2, 1, 9, 8, 7, 6, ...\}$ are the reduced numbers in the eight-times table. They are the reverse of the one-times (or the set of consecutive numbers).

The 'magical' nine-times table shows a surprising result!

$9 \times 1 =$	9	9
$9 \times 2 =$	18	9
$9 \times 3 =$	27	9
$9 \times 4 =$	36	9
$9 \times 5 =$	45	9

$9 \times 6 =$	54	9
$9 \times 7 =$	63	9
$9 \times 8 =$	72	9
$9 \times 9 =$	81	9
$9 \times 10 =$	90	9

$9 \times 11 =$	99	9
$9 \times 12 =$	108	9

Notice that the product column has answers that are the reverse of each other.

What is the sum of the reduced numbers of the pairs ...
(9×1) and (9×8) ?
(9×2) and (9×7) ?
(9×3) and (9×6) ?
(9×4) and (9×5) ?

The secret is the key number 9

A digital computer

A simple way to perform multiplication by 9, of any number from 1 to 9 can be done by using both hands. Suppose the question is 4×9.
● Hold up your two hands, with the palms away from you.
● Bend down the fourth finger from the left, on your left hand.
● Your answer is now visible!

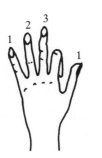
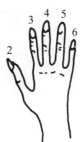

3 – 6

Try 8×9. From left to right count 8 and put that finger down. Answer?

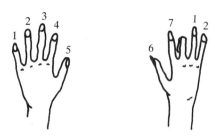

Now multiply several numbers by 9. Find their reduced numbers. What conclusion can you make about the sum of the digits of *any* multiple of 9? Apply this conclusion to determine which of the following numbers are evenly divisible by 9.

477   8766   13845

Reason: Let 100*a*, 10*b* and *c* be the digits.

$$\therefore \quad 100a + 10b + c = a(99 + 1) + b(9 + 1) + c$$
$$= (99a + 9b) + (a + b + c)$$

↑   ↑
Divisible by 9   *Remainder*

Suppose 15 is divided by 9.
- What is the remainder?
- What is the sum of the digits 1 and 5?

Your answers should be the same. Try other examples.

The sum of the digits of any number (i.e. its reduced number) is always equal to the *remainder* obtained when the number is divided by 9.

The remainders in the nine-times table are no exception to this rule. The remainders of the multiples of 9 are 0. Suppose 27 is divided by 9. It could be said that it goes three times or two times with a remainder of 9 (equal to its reduced number)!

Casting out nines

Division is a short method of repeated subtraction, e.g. 24÷9 goes twice [(24 − 9) − 9], with a remainder of 6. This method is usually time-consuming, so division is preferred. By finding the reduced number, we obtain the remainder much more quickly.

> *Step 1*   Take any 3 digit number, e.g. 582
> *Step 2*   Find its reduced number. 5 + 8 + 2 → 15 → 6
> *Step 3*   Divide 582 by 9. Remainder?

Accountants often check calculations by this means.

ADDITION

                  reduced number

$47 + \rightarrow 11 \rightarrow 2 +$ $5 \times 9 +$ Remainder 2

$28 \quad \rightarrow 10 \rightarrow 1$ $3 \times 9 +$ Remainder 1

$\overline{75} \quad \rightarrow 12 \rightarrow \boxed{3}$ $\overline{8 \times 9} +$ Remainder 3

When no mistake has been made, the reduced number of the question will agree with the reduced number of the answer.

SUBTRACTION

$4787 \quad \rightarrow 26 \rightarrow \quad 8$

$- 235 \quad \rightarrow 10 \rightarrow -1$

$\overline{4552} \quad \rightarrow 16 \rightarrow \quad \boxed{7}$

MULTIPLICATION

$19 \times \xrightarrow{\hspace{2cm}} 10 \rightarrow 1 \times$

$12 \xrightarrow{\hspace{2cm}} 3$

$\overline{38}$

190

$\overline{228} \xrightarrow{\hspace{1.5cm}} 12 \rightarrow \boxed{3}$

DIVISION

$9\overline{)823} \rightarrow 13$

$\quad\overline{91}$ remainder 4

Tempting tricks

1. Impossible 37

- Choose any 3-digit number with all digits the same   333
- Find its reduced number   9
- Divide the original number by the reduced answer $9\overline{)333}$
- Your answer should always be 37   37

2. The Lost Digit

- Write down any 4-digit number (all different digits)   47$\not{6}$2
- Find the reduced number $\longrightarrow 18 \longrightarrow$ 9
- Cross out one of the original digits
- Subtract the reduced number from the   472
- 3 digits (in order) $- \quad 9$
- Result? $\overline{463}$

To determine the number crossed out, find the reduced number of the final answer and subtract it from 9. The result will be the crossed out digit. $(4 + 6 + 3 \rightarrow 13 \rightarrow 4; 9 - 4 = 5)$

3. To Guess a Person's Age

- Ask the person to write any 3-digit number and rearrange the   314
  digits to form another number   143
- Subtract the smaller from the larger   314
       $\underline{-143}$
       171+
- Add the age $\underline{\ \ 21}$
- Answer?   192

> The secret is to find the reduced number of the answer (3) then keep adding 9s until you obtain the number you think is *nearest* to the person's age. (12? 21? 30? 39?)

4. An Addition Trick

Let someone make up a problem by writing a series of large numbers, one below the other. Cast out nines as the person writes down the numbers, to find the reduced number of the whole set of numbers. Turn your back while the total is found.

The person then circles a number (not zero) in the answer and tells you the remaining digits. You are then able to say the circled number. How?

Obtain the reduced number of the numbers called out, then subtract it from the previous reduced number that you calculated. (If the second number is larger than the first, add 9 to the first root before subtracting.) If the two answers are the same, then a 9 was circled.

The following exercises all give answers that have reduced numbers of 9

5.
- Write any number.
- Rearrange the digits in any order.
- Subtract the smaller from the larger.

6.
- Write any number.
- Find the reduced number.
- Subtract it from the original number.

7.
- Write down your telephone number.
- Rearrange the digits.
- Subtract the smaller from the larger.

8.
- Write any 3-digit number.
- Find the reduced number.
- Multiply this by 8.
- Add your product to the original number.

9. 1089

- Write down any 3-digit number that is not palindromic (with the hundreds differing from the unit digit by 2 or more).
- Reverse the digits.
- Subtract the smaller from the larger (99 = 099).
- Add this answer to its reverse.

Did you get 1089? What is its reduced number?

Example :

$$
\begin{array}{r}
825 \\
-528 \\
\hline
297 \\
792 \\
\hline
1089
\end{array}
$$

1089 has interesting features.

$$
\begin{array}{rcl}
1089 \times 1 &=& 1\ 0\ 8\ 9 \\
\times 2 &=& 2\ 1\ 7\ 8 \\
\times 3 &=& 3\ 2\ 6\ 7 \\
\times 4 &=& 4\ 3\ 5\ 6 \\
\times 5 &=& 5\ 4\ 4\ 5 \\
\times 6 &=& 6\ 5\ 3\ 4 \\
\times 7 &=& 7\ 6\ 2\ 3 \\
\times 8 &=& 8\ 7\ 1\ 2 \\
\times 9 &=& 9\ 8\ 0\ 1 \\
& & \downarrow\ \uparrow\ \downarrow\ \uparrow
\end{array}
$$

$\rightarrow$ Reduced number 9

Note the vertical number patterns indicated by the arrows.

10. An April Fool's Trick

- Write down any 3-digit number with first and last digits differing by more than one (e.g. 582, 380).
- Reverse the order.
- Subtract the smaller number from the larger.
- Reverse the digits of the difference and add this number to the difference.
- Multiply the answer by one million.
- Subtract 733 361 573.
- Then : under each 2 in your answer write the letter P;
  under each 3 in your answer write the letter L;
  under each 4, write R;
  under each 5, write O;
  under each 6, write F;
  under each 7, write A;
  under each 8, write I.
- Now, read the letters backwards.

Variations can be made after the stage of multiplying by one million, in order to obtain a different message, providing it does not contain more than ten different letters.

11. Fresno (credited to Dale Seymour, Creative Publications, USA)

The object of this game is to form the highest *single* digit (9) from given integers. Students may say their favourite numbers less than ten, polyhedra dice may be rolled or numbered cards may be turned to give the 3 digits. Only 4 operations and grouping symbols may be used.

7

	DIGITS			WORKING	HIGHEST NUMBER
Game 1	4	8	3	8 + 4 − 3	9
Game 2	5	3	2	3(5 − 2)	9
Game 3					
Game 4					

SCORE BOX

→ | 9 | 9 | | |

Any number of games may be played with a *time limit* (say two minutes) for each one. At the end of each game the highest number must be recorded in the last column and in a chosen position in the score box.

The highest answer wins, with 9999 being a perfect score.

This game could be varied by finding the *lowest* single digit, instead of the highest.

Why is it so?

- Write down any three numbers less than ten, e.g. 3, 4 and 7.
- Make all the six possible 2-digit numbers using these three numbers.
- Find their sum.
- Calculate the sum of the original numbers.
- Divide the first total by the second.
- Answer?

Repeat the operations for other combinations of numbers.

$$34$$
$$37$$
$$43$$
$$47$$
$$73$$
$$74$$
$$14\overline{)308}$$
$$22$$

Algebraically: Let a, b, c represent the numbers less than ten.

$$\therefore 10a + b$$
$$10a + c$$
$$10b + a$$
$$10b + c$$
$$10c + a$$
$$\underline{10c + b}$$
$$\overline{22a + 22b + 22c}$$

$$22a + 22b + 22c$$
$$= 22(a + b + c)$$
$$\therefore \frac{22(a + b + c)}{(a + b + c)}$$
$$= 22$$

Important revision work can be done with reduced numbers. It is a challenge to find the length of each cycle or period. Complete the following exercises, underlining one period, where possible. Some are done for you.

1. Consecutive numbers

	1	2	3	4	5	6	7	8	9	10	11	12	13	14	15	....	....
Reduced numbers	1	2	3	4	5	6	7	8	9	1	2	....	....	....	....	....	....

2. Even numbers

2	4	6	8	10	12	14	16	18	20	22	24	....	....
2	4	6	8	1	3	....	....	....	....	....	....	....	....

3. Odd numbers *The god delights in an odd number.* (Virgil)

1	3	5	7	9	....	13	15	:....	19	....	23	....	....
1	3	5	7	9	2	....	....	....	....	....	....	....	....

Did you know that the sum of consecutive odd numbers gives a square number?

e.g. $1 + 3 = 4$ (2^2)
$1 + 3 + 5 = 9$ (3^2)
$1 + 3 + 5 + 7 = 16$ (4^2)

Rule: The sum of the first n odd numbers is equal to n^2.

∴ the sum of the first 1000 odd numbers $= (1000)^2$
$$= 1\,000\,000$$

This result was proved geometrically by the ancient Greeks.

What type of number do you get if you add ....
- an even number to an even number?
- an odd number to an odd number?
- an even number to an odd number?

What are your conclusions?

The square of an odd number is always odd. True or False?

The cube of an even number is always even. True or false?

* Which five odd numbers have a sum of 14?

For the early Christians and the Pythagoreans, maleness was associated with odd numbers, femaleness with even ones.

Complete this table:

ROW		SUM OF EACH HORIZONTAL ROW	CUBES	AVERAGE OF FIRST AND LAST NOS	SQUARES
1	1	1	1	1	1^2
2	3 5	8	2^3	4	2^2
3	7 9 11	27	3^3		
4	13 15 17 19				
5	21 23 25 27 29				
6					
7					

Notice the connections!

4. Square numbers General term: $\frac{n}{2}(2n) = n^2$

(Also called *figurate numbers*)

1	4	9	16	25	36	49	64	81	100	....	144	....	....
1	4	9	7	7	....	....	....	....	....	....	....	....	....

What is the period?

Looking at the sequence of numbers, can you determine which of the following *cannot* be perfect squares?

$$15476 \qquad 98596 \qquad 45269$$

A valuable rule for squaring any number ending in 5
- Square the last digit (5).
- Write down the answer.
- Multiply the number in the tens column by the consecutive number above it.
- Write this product in front of the 25.

e.g. 35^2
$5^2 = 25$
$4 \times 3 = 12$

$35^2 = 1225$

Work out 65^2, 85^2, 105^2 in a similar way.

5. Cubic numbers

1^3	2^3	3^3	4^3	5^3	6^3	7^3	8^3	9^3	10^3
1	8	27	....	....	....	243	....	....	....

reduced number	1	8	9

6. Triangular numbers general term: $\frac{n}{2}(n + 1)$

1	3	6	10	15	21	....	....	....	....
1	3	....	1	....	3	....	....	....	....

Note: The sum of any two consecutive triangular numbers is a square number.
e.g. $1 + \ 3 = 4 \quad (2^2)$
        $3 + \ 6 = 9 \quad (3^2)$
        $6 + 10 = 16 \quad (4^2)$ etc.

Also, the sum of any number of consecutive triangular numbers is a tetrahedral number.

$$1 = 1$$
$$1 + 3 = 4$$
$$1 + 3 + 6 = 10$$
$$1 + 3 + 6 + 10 = 20 \text{ etc.}$$

7. **Pentagonal numbers** general term: $\frac{n}{2}(3n - 1)$

1	5	12	22	35	51	70	92	117	....	....
1	5	3	....	....	....	....	....	....	....	

8. **Hexagonal numbers** General term: $\frac{n}{2}(4n - 2) = n(2n - 1)$

1	6	15	28	45	66	....	....	....
1	6	6	....	....	....	....	....	....

9. An arithmetic series

2	5	8	11	14	17	20	....	26	....	32
2	....	....	2	....	....	2	....	....	....	....

10. A geometric series

1	3	9	27	81	243	729	....	....	....
1	....	....	9	9	....	....	....	....	....

On 1 August, 1964 (1 – 8 – 64) the day, month and year were all in a geometric series. Each term was eight times the previous one:

$$\frac{1}{8} = \frac{8}{64}$$

How many such dates have occurred, and will occur, this century?

Fibonacci numbers

Known as Leonardo da Pisa, the great Italian mathematician Fibonacci (AD 1170 – 1250) was educated in Barbary and travelled extensively. In his book *Liber Abaci* (1202), for centuries a standard work on algebra and arithmetic, he advocated the adoption of Arabic notation.

As early in the history of numbers as AD 1225, he became aware of negative numbers!

Here is the sequence which Fibonacci discovered. Form the next numbers by adding the previous pairs:

	1	1	2	3	5	8	13	21	34	55	....
reduced number	1	1	2	3	5	8	4	3	7	1	....

Continue until you have the twenty-sixth number.

You can use the formula $F_n = F_{n-2} + F_{n-1}$ to find successive terms, where F represents a Fibonacci number and n is an *ordinal* number.

This sequence has a period of 24, one of the longest you will find in this work.

The reduced numbers should be:

1 1 2 3 5 8 4 3 7 1 8 9 8 8 7 6 4 1 5 6 2 8 1 9.

Look carefully at the twenty-four digits. Are they formed in the same way as the original Fibonacci sequence?

When they are arranged in a 6×4 matrix, more interesting patterns emerge.

$$
\begin{array}{llllll}
1 & 5 & 7 & 8 & 4 & 2 \quad \text{.... digits in } \tfrac{1}{7} \\
1 & 8 & 1 & 8 & 1 & 8 \quad \text{.... repetition of pairs} \\
2 & 4 & 8 & 7 & 5 & 1 \quad \text{.... reverse of line 1} \\
3 & 3 & 9 & 6 & 6 & 9 \quad \text{.... multiple of 3}
\end{array}
$$

Similarly a 4×6 matrix shows other features.

$$
\begin{array}{llll}
1 & 4 & 8 & 5 \\
1 & 3 & 8 & 6 \\
2 & 7 & 7 & 2 \\
3 & 1 & 6 & 8 \\
5 & 8 & 4 & 1 \\
8 & 9 & 1 & 9
\end{array}
$$

Rows 1 and 5 are reversed
Rows 2 and 4 are 'matching'
Row 3 is 'palindromic'

By writing alternate reduced numbers, a palindromic arrangement is formed.
reduced numbers ● 1 2 5 4 7 8 | 8 7 4 5 2 1 ....
Similarly a more regular pattern is formed with the remaining alternate numbers, again palindromic about 1.
reduced numbers ● 1 3 8 3 1 9 8 6 | 6 8 9 1 3 8 3 1 ....

Fibonacci Numbers in Physics

The ancient Greeks discovered that light travels in straight lines. A second important discovery about light was made by Heron of Alexandria who, when experimenting with mirrors, noticed that any beam of light directed towards a mirror at an angle would bounce off again at an equal angle (the angle of incidence equals the angle of reflection).

In how many ways can light travel through a pair of face-to-face glass plates?

Number of reflections

Number of different paths

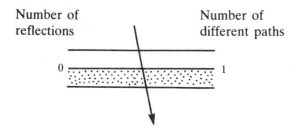

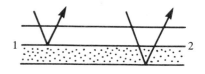

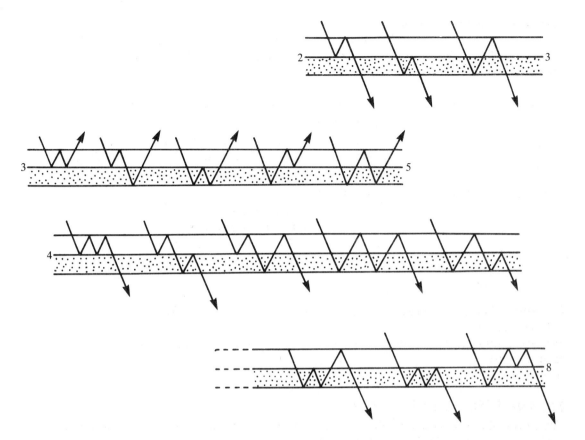

Rule: For m reflections there are F_{m+2} paths possible.

Many valuable exercises can be worked out using the Fibonacci sequence. A code is used to name the elements of the sequence, i.e. $F_1 = 1$, $F_2 = 1$, $F_3 = 2$, $F_4 = 3$, etc.

Write down the list, in a column, as far as F_{25}. A calculator may be used to check your additions! Alternatively, use the following formula to evaluate any given term.

$$F_n = \frac{1}{\sqrt{5}}\left[\left(\frac{1+\sqrt{5}}{2}\right)^n - \left(\frac{1-\sqrt{5}}{2}\right)^n\right]$$

Verifying F_2 when $n = 2$:

$$F^2 = \frac{1}{\sqrt{5}}\left[\left(\frac{1+\sqrt{5}}{2}\right)^2 - \left(\frac{1-\sqrt{5}}{2}\right)^2\right]$$

$$= \frac{1}{\sqrt{5}}\left[\left(\frac{1+2\sqrt{5}+5}{4}\right) - \left(\frac{1-2\sqrt{5}+5}{4}\right)\right]$$

$$= \frac{1}{\sqrt{5}}\left[\frac{6+2\sqrt{5}-6+2\sqrt{5}}{4}\right]$$

$$= \frac{1}{\sqrt{5}}\left[\frac{4\sqrt{5}}{4}\right]$$

$$= 1$$

Exercises

a. Calculate the sum of the first *five* terms. What is the difference between your answer and F_7? Try the formula: $F_1 + F_2 + \dots + F_n = F_{n+2} - 1$ where n stands for the nth Fibonacci number.

b. Find the sum of the first *nine* terms. Is it 1 less than F_{11}?

c. Test this principle by making up further examples yourself.

d. Verify your results by substituting in the general formula for the sum of n terms: $F_n = F_{n+2} - 1$ where F_n means the sum of n terms.

e. Find the sum of the first four even-coded Fibonacci numbers $(F_2 + F_4 + F_6 + F_8)$, then find the relationship between this answer and another Fibonacci number. Test with further examples.

f. Calculate the sum of the first *four* odd-coded terms $(F_1 + F_3 + F_5 + F_7)$. What is the connection with the 8th term? Can you guess the sum of the first *eight* terms of the odd sequence, without adding?

g. Evaluate:
$$F_2 \div F_1 =$$
$$F_3 \div F_2 =$$
$$F_4 \div F_3 =$$

What happens as n increases? As n becomes very large, what value does $\dfrac{F_n}{F_{n-1}}$ approach?

h. Complete the following patterns:
$$F_2 + F_6 = \dots (\ )^2$$
$$F_2 + F_6 + F_{10} = \dots (\ )^2$$
$$F_2 + F_6 + F_{10} + F_{14} = \dots (\ )^2$$
$$F_2 + F_6 + F_{10} + F_{14} + F_{18} = \dots (\ )^2.$$

i. Write down the *squares* of the first eight terms of the sequence. Add each pair of consecutive squares to make a new sequence. What do you notice?

Have you noticed? Every third term in the Fibonacci sequence is even, every fourth is divisible by 3, every fifth by 5 and every fifteenth by 10.

In 1225, the Holy Roman Emperor Frederick II went to Pisa with a group of mathematicians, to test Leonardo publicly against John of Palermo. John was the court scholar, and his skill in solving numerical problems was renowned.

One problem given at the tournament was:

Find a square which remains a square if it is decreased by 5 or increased by 5.

Obviously the answer is not an integer. After a short time, Fibonacci gave the correct answer,

$$\frac{1681}{144} \text{ or } \left(\frac{41}{12}\right)^2$$

When 5 is subtracted it remains a square:

$$\frac{961}{144} = \left(\frac{31}{12}\right)^2$$

and when 5 is added it remains a square:

$$\frac{2401}{144} = \left(\frac{49}{12}\right)^2$$

The second posed by John was to solve the equation

$$x^3 + 2x^2 + 10x = 20$$

14

Fibonacci's answer, expressed in sexagesimal (numbers with a unit base of 60), was:
$$x = 1^{0}22^{i}7^{ii}42^{iii}33^{iv}4^{v}40^{vi}\ !$$
The third problem was widely copied by later writers:

'3 men agree to share a certain sum of money, their shares to be in the ratios $\frac{1}{2}$, $\frac{1}{3}$ and $\frac{1}{6}$. While they were making their division, they were surprised by an enemy and each snatched what he could. Later the first man gave up half of what he had, the second gave up one third, and the third, one sixth. This money was then divided among them equally and each then had the share to which he was entitled.
What was the total sum?'

[The problem is indeterminate, the smallest sum being 47.]

Fibonacci's *Practica geometriae* (1220) systematised the subject matter of practical geometry. It treated squares and square roots, proportion, measurement of areas and volumes and the use of a surveying instrument called the *quadrans*. This was a geometric square which was a square framework with a movable pointer mounted at one corner. The instrument could be levelled by means of a plumb line and angles of elevation or depression could be found by sighting along the pointer. The sides of the square were divided into equal segments thus providing a simple way of computing the ratio of the unknown object.

Besides *Practica geometriae*, Fibonacci also wrote *Liber quadratorum* (1225) and the *Flos*, a book on algebra.

It is believed that Fibonacci was the first to use this sign in 1220. Coming from the Latin *radix* (meaning root), it is much more complex than today's radical sign ($\sqrt{}$), which is probably a distortion of the letter *r* from sixteenth century Germany.

This symbol was created in 1525 by Christoff Rudolff, a German mathematician, to represent the cube root. Today's sign probably came from French writings of the seventeenth century.

* *Puzzle.* Is it possible to construct a triangle whose sides are 3 different Fibonacci numbers?

A Calculation Conundrum
- Ask your partner to write down any 2 single-digit numbers, one under the other.
- Add them to find a third number. Write it underneath.
- Now add the second and third numbers (repeating addition).
- Then add the third and fourth numbers.
- Continue doing this until there are 10 numbers in the column.
- While this is being done you keep your back turned.
- After the 10 numbers are completed you turn around and immediately write the sum of all 10 numbers.

How is it done?
The secret is to multiply the *fourth* number from the bottom by 11.

Lucas numbers

The Frenchman Edouard Lucas (1842-1891) is reputed to have given the Fibonacci sequence its name. His *Théorie des Nombres* is a fascinating book on the theory of numbers.

A sequence of numbers, named after Lucas, has a growth pattern similar to Fibonacci's.

Number :   1   3   4   7   11   18   29   ....
Code : L_1 L_2 L_3 L_4 L_5 L_6 L_7 ....

a. Write down the next twenty three terms.
b. Record the set of reduced numbers. What is the period?

Notice that the reduced numbers form a sequence in the same way as the Fibonacci and Lucas sequences (by adding the previous pair of numbers to obtain the next number)! When alternate numbers are written down, palindromic triples appear.

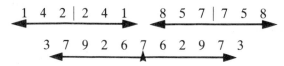

c. Write down the set of Lucas primes.
d. Which Lucas number is composed of 3 consecutive digits?
e. Find $L_1 + L_3 + L_5 + L_7$.
   Is your answer two less than L_8?
f. Work out $L_2 + L_4 + L_6$.
   What is its relationship with L_7?
g. For any four consecutive Lucas numbers (a, b, c, d), show $c^2 - b^2 = ad$
h. The sum of the Fibonacci and Lucas reduced numbers gives :

```
FIBONACCI :     1 1 2 3 5 8 4 3 7 1 8 9 8 8 7 6 4 1 5 6 2 8 1 9
LUCAS :         1 3 4 7 2 9 2*2 4 6 1 7 8 6 5 2 7 9 7 7 5 3 8 2*
                *2 4 6 1 7 8 6 5 2 7 9 7 7 5 3 8 2*1 3 4 7 2 9 2
```

The total generates seventeen places of the Lucas numbers! (between the asterisks)

Palindromic numbers

In the fourteenth row of Pascal's triangle (see page 21), we find the numbers 1001, 2002, 3003. These are palindromic numbers, because they read the same forwards and backwards. There are also palindromic numbers in the fifteenth and sixteenth rows.

Activity

Add 24 to its reversed digits. The answer (66) is palindromic. This is a simple example of only one step. Given enough time and patience, any number can be transformed into a palindrome by following these rules:
- Take any number.
- Reverse its digits and add the number formed to the preceding one.
- Continue doing this until a palindrome appears.

This example has 3 steps.
(from 89 to 8 813 200 023 188 takes twenty four steps!)

e.g.

$$168+$$
$$\underline{861}$$
$$1029+$$
$$\underline{9201}$$
$$10230+$$
$$\underline{03201}$$
$$\boxed{13431}$$

Now complete the following table:

Number	Number of Steps	Palindrome
24	1	66
68	3	1111
123	1	444
241		
364		
472		
553		
561		

It should be clear that 24 and 42 will both give the same result in the same number of steps. 68 and 86 will do the same.

Suppose all the numbers up to 100 were chosen. How many would you have to investigate altogether? Remember, some are palindromes already.
List those that take only one step.
These take 2 steps: 19, 28, 37, 39, 46, 48, 49, 57, 58, 67
These take 3 steps: 59, 68
These take 4 steps: 69, 78
This takes 6 steps: 79.
A calculator or computer is a great asset when testing larger numbers!

To ponder
* ● What is the only palindromic year this century?
* ● How many palindromic dates are there between now and the year 2000? (e.g. 19 – 3 – 91)
  ● How many palindromic years will be in the twenty-first century?
* ● Write down all the palindromic times between 12 midnight and 12 midday (as shown on a digital clock or watch).
  ● Study your answers to these: 1^2, 11^2, 111^2, 1111^2, 11111^2, 111111^2, ...

Make a list of all the palindromic numbers less than 200 and underneath each write the corresponding reduced number. Commence with 11, 22, 33, 44, 55, ..., 191. You should find a surprising set of reduced numbers!

If continued into the tens of thousands, the following table shows the patterns generated by the reduced numbers. Note the regularity of the dots, which signify 'missing' digits. The period is very large!

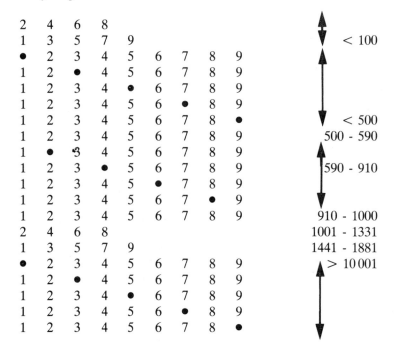

									Range
2	4	6	8						
1	3	5	7	9					< 100
•	2	3	4	5	6	7	8	9	
1	2	•	4	5	6	7	8	9	
1	2	3	4	•	6	7	8	9	
1	2	3	4	5	6	•	8	9	
1	2	3	4	5	6	7	8	•	< 500
1	2	3	4	5	6	7	8	9	500 - 590
1	•	3	4	5	6	7	8	9	
1	2	3	•	5	6	7	8	9	590 - 910
1	2	3	4	5	•	7	8	9	
1	2	3	4	5	6	7	•	9	
1	2	3	4	5	6	7	8	9	910 - 1000
2	4	6	8						1001 - 1331
1	3	5	7	9					1441 - 1881
•	2	3	4	5	6	7	8	9	> 10 001
1	2	•	4	5	6	7	8	9	
1	2	3	4	•	6	7	8	9	
1	2	3	4	5	6	•	8	9	
1	2	3	4	5	6	7	8	•	

Spirolaterals are visual patterns done on various grid papers, that form interesting closed or open designs. A closed pattern returns to its starting point while an open one repeats infinitely. Spirolaterals may have all right-hand turns, all left-hand turns, or a combination. The angle of turning remains constant.

Unit lengths on the grid paper vary according to specific instructions or orders.

Closed figures have line or point symmetry.

On the computer, Papert's Turtle Programs (using the language Logo), illustrate another way spirolaterals may be drawn.

Spirolaterals were investigated around 1973 by Frank Odds, a British biochemist. He called them spirolaterals – where 'spiro' meant the curved patterns formed and 'lateral' meant the flat surface.

These spirolaterals are of the reduced palindromic numbers less than 100 i.e. $\{2, 4, 6, 8, 1, 3, 5, 7, 9\}$.

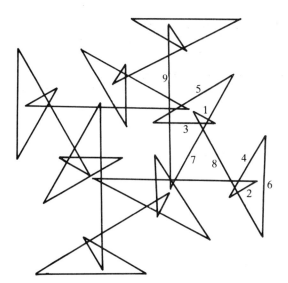

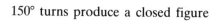

150° turns produce a closed figure

120° turns give an open figure

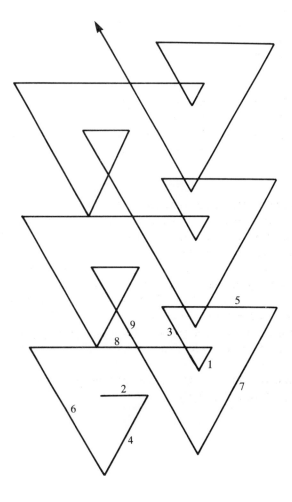

19

90° turns generate a closed one

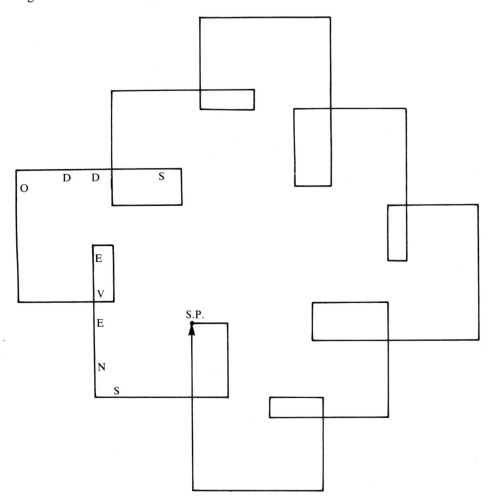

Pascal's triangle

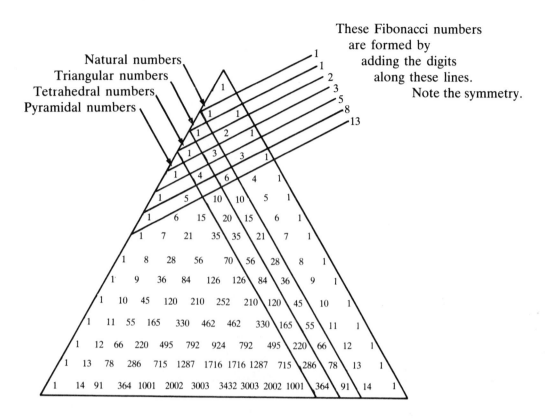

Natural numbers
Triangular numbers
Tetrahedral numbers
Pyramidal numbers

These Fibonacci numbers
are formed by
adding the digits
along these lines.
Note the symmetry.

```
                    1
                    1
              1     2
            1   1   3
          1   2   1 5
        1   3   3   1  8
      1   4   6   4   1  13
    1   5  10  10   5   1
  1   6  15  20  15   6   1
1   7  21  35  35  21   7   1
1   8  28  56  70  56  28   8   1
1   9  36  84 126 126  84  36   9   1
1  10  45 120 210 252 210 120  45  10   1
1  11  55 165 330 462 462 330 165  55  11   1
1  12  66 220 495 792 924 792 495 220  66  12   1
1  13  78 286 715 1287 1716 1716 1287 715 286  78  13   1
1  14  91 364 1001 2002 3003 3432 3003 2002 1001 364  91  14   1
```

It was mentioned on page 16 that Pascal's triangle contains some palindromic numbers. Besides those mentioned, what other palindromic numbers appear?

Pascal's triangle was known to the Chinese in the early fourteenth century but not published in Europe till the sixteenth century.

It also contains some startling patterns of equilateral triangles. When all the odd numbers are coloured, this is the result (as far as the fifteenth row).

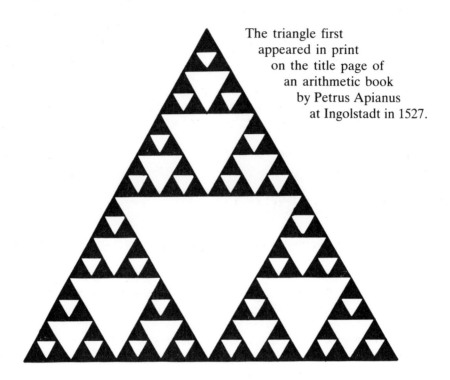

The triangle first
appeared in print
on the title page of
an arithmetic book
by Petrus Apianus
at Ingolstadt in 1527.

When the evens are coloured, the 'negative' is formed.

An attractive wall chart can be made by tessellating these designs together, into hexagons or overall patterns. The designs may be done on square, isometric or hexagonal grid paper.

Blaise Pascal was born in 1623 at Clermont and died in 1662, in Paris. A geometer and philosopher, he invented the barometer and a calculating machine.

Pascal's correspondence with Fermat laid down the principles of his Theory of Probability. In his triangle, the sum of the rows (horizontally) gives the total number of combinations possible within a group, and is always a power of 2. For example, to determine the probability of any boy-girl combination in a family of six children, the numbers in the sixth row are added. These are 1, 6, 15, 20, 15, 6 and 1 which give a total of sixty four.

The *least* likely combination (all boys or all girls) is indicated by the ones at each end, giving the chance as 1 in 64.

The next most likely combination (five boys and one girl or vice versa), gives 6 in 64 (3 in 32).

The middle number, 20, gives the chances of having three boys and three girls. i.e. 20 in 64 or 5 in 16.

Gematria

The priests of Babylon are believed to have started the practice of gematria or assigning 'mystical' numbers to words. Assume that the letters of the alphabet have the numerical place value they hold, i.e. $A = 1$, $B = 2$, ..., $J = 10$,...., $Z = 26$. What would be the numerical value of your first name? (Add the numbers to obtain the value.) The mystical numbers were thought to be very important, for if two people had the same number, they were supposed to be compatible.

The Greeks also used gematria. It was also natural for early Christians to take up the numerological ideas of the Greeks and Jews. The early religious symbol of the dove was probably adopted because the Greek letters *alpha* and *omega* add to 801, the same number as *peristera*, Greek for 'dove'.

The word *amen* had a gematric value of 99 when written in Greek, hence early Christian prayers had 99 at the end!

Persistence numbers

A number's persistence is the number of steps required to reduce it to a single digit by repeated multiplication.

$$e.g. \; 89 \rightarrowtail 72 \rightarrowtail 14 \rightarrowtail 4 \text{ has a persistence of } 3.$$

The smallest persistence number is 1, which occurs in all numbers containing a zero,

$$e.g. \quad 10 \rightarrowtail 0$$
$$304 \rightarrowtail 0.$$

Think of five other numbers with a persistence number of 1.
What is the first palindromic number greater than 100 that has a persistence of 1?

Find the persistence numbers of:

28	31	49	134	277	385	535	944

The *smallest* number of persistence 2 is 25 and the smallest number of persistence 3 is 39. The smallest persistence 4 number is between 70 and 79. Work it out. The smallest number of persistence 5 is 679 while 6788 is the smallest one for persistence 6.

N.J.A. Sloane of Bell Laboratories determined by computer that no number less than 10^{50} has a persistence number greater than 11!

The persistence operation can be applied to base numbers with interesting results.

Naturally, all base 2 numbers have only one step or a persistence of 1. The answers have to be either 0 or 1.

persistence answer

$1_{10} = \quad 1_2 \rightarrowtail 1$

$2_{10} = \quad 10_2 \rightarrowtail 0$

$3_{10} = \quad 11_2 \rightarrowtail 1$

$4_{10} = 100_2 \rightarrowtail 0$

$5_{10} = 101_2 \rightarrowtail 0$

Copy and continue this exercise as far as 111_2 (15_{10}).

In base 3, the second answer obtained when working out the persistence is either 0 or a power of 2.

Study this table :

$$
\begin{aligned}
3_{10} &= 10_3 \rightarrowtail 0 \\
4_{10} &= 11_3 \rightarrowtail 1 \quad (2^0) \\
5_{10} &= 12_3 \rightarrowtail 2 \quad (2^1) \\
6_{10} &= 20_3 \rightarrowtail 0 \\
7_{10} &= 21_3 \rightarrowtail 2^1 \\
8_{10} &= 22_3 \rightarrowtail 4 \quad (2^2) \\
9_{10} &= 100_3 \rightarrowtail 0 \\
10_{10} &= 101_3 \rightarrowtail 0 \\
11_{10} &= 102_3 \rightarrowtail 0 \\
12_{10} &= 110_3 \rightarrowtail 0 \\
13_{10} &= 111_3 \rightarrowtail 1 \quad (2^0) \\
14_{10} &= 112_3 \rightarrowtail 2^1 \\
15_{10} &= 120_3 \rightarrowtail 0 \\
16_{10} &= 121_3 \rightarrowtail 2^1 \\
17_{10} &= 122_3 \rightarrowtail 4 \quad (2^2) \\
18_{10} &= 200_3 \rightarrowtail 0 \\
19_{10} &= 201_3 \rightarrowtail 0 \\
20_{10} &= 202_3 \rightarrowtail 0 \\
21_{10} &= 210_3 \rightarrowtail 0 \\
22_{10} &= 211_3 \rightarrowtail 2^1
\end{aligned}
$$

The persistence answers form repeating periods. How many elements in each period?

Calculator capers

a. Assume that the letters of the alphabet are given their numerical value, i.e. A = 1, B = 2, C = 3, ... The aim is to find a word (or two words?) such that when the values are *multiplied*, the result is exactly one million.

* **b.** Assign the letters the reversed values, i.e. A = 26, B = 25, C = 24, ..., Z = 1. This time, the aim is to determine one word with a value *as close as possible* to one million (above or below). Again the values are multiplied.

c. Work out $999\,999\,999 \times \underline{12\,345\,679}$

* **d.** Calculate 4 numbers that add to 45 so that if 2 is added to the first number, 2 is subtracted from the second, the third is doubled and the fourth halved, the answers are always 10.

e. Multiply 37 by 3, 6, 9, 12, 15, 18, 21, 24 and 27. You will notice the answers are palindromic. The sum of the digits will equal the number by which you multiplied 37.
e.g. $37 \times 3 = 111 \quad 1 + 1 + 1 = 3$, the multiplier.

f. Write down a number consisting of all the digits 1 to 9. Reverse the digits three times and add each figure to the original number. To this answer add 2.
Did you get $2\,222\,222\,222$?
What is this *in words*?

Zapping

Zapping is finding the sum of the squares of the digits of any number, repeatedly until a single answer is obtained. Often zapping must be continued for quite a while to obtain a result.

e.g. $12 \nearrow 1^2 + 2^2$
$\quad\quad = 1 + 4$
$\quad\quad = 5$

$31 \nearrow 3^2 + 1^2$
$\quad\quad = 9 + 1$
$\quad\quad = 10$
$10 \nearrow 1^2 + 0^2$
$\quad\quad = 1 + 0$
$\quad\quad = 1$
i.e. $31 \nearrow 10 \nearrow 1$

Numbers like 31 which zap to 1 are called happy numbers.

Another happy number is $1300 \nearrow 1 + 9 + 0 + 0 \quad\quad 10 \nearrow 1 + 0$
$\quad\quad\quad\quad\quad\quad\quad\quad = 10 \quad\quad\quad\quad\quad\quad = 1$
$\quad\quad\quad \therefore \ 1300 \nearrow 10 \nearrow 1$

$68 \nearrow 36 + 64 \quad\quad 100 \nearrow 1 + 0 + 0$
$\quad\quad\quad = 100 \quad\quad\quad\quad\quad = 1$
$\quad\quad \therefore \ 68 \nearrow 100 \nearrow 1$

What is the first happy number after 10?

* Work out the lowest digits formed when zapping the numbers between 10 and 50 (inclusive). How many happy numbers are there altogether?

Try 86, 129, 912.

Is 37 happy? Go as far as you can.

Factorials $(1 \times 2 \times 3 \ .... \ \times n)$

In how many ways can three different numbers be arranged? Take, for example, 1, 2 and 3. Altogether there are six ways, generating these numbers: 123, 132, 213, 231, 312, 321. The same answer (6) is obtained by multiplying 3 by 2 by 1. The number of ways is called factorial n and is written $n!$

e.g. $5! = 5 \times 4 \times 3 \times 2 \times 1$
$\quad\quad = 120$

Complete:

3!	$= 3 \times 2 \times 1$		$= 6$
4!	$= 4 \times 3 \times 2 \times 1$		$= 24$
5!	$= 5 \times 4 \times 3 \times 2 \times 1$		$= 120$
6!	$=$	....	$=$ ....
7!	$=$	....	$=$ ....
8!	$=$	....	$=$ ....

This pattern generates prime answers:

$3! - 2! + 1!$ $\quad\quad\quad\quad\quad\quad\quad\quad\quad = \quad\ 5$
$4! - 3! + 2! - 1!$ $\quad\quad\quad\quad\quad\quad\quad = \quad 19$
$5! - 4! + 3! - 2! + 1!$ $\quad\quad\quad\quad\quad = \quad 101$
$6! - 5! + 4! - 3! + 2! - 1!$ $\quad\quad\quad = \quad 619$
$7! - 6! + 5! - 4! + 3! - 2! + 1!$ $\quad = 4421$

Prime numbers

Prime numbers have only two factors – themselves and 1. Two is the only even prime. One is not considered a prime as it does not fit the conditions of the definition. Also zero is considered to be neither prime nor composite.

Twin primes differ by 2 and have an even number between them. The only exception is the first pair of primes (2, 3), sometimes referred to as Siamese twins! Examples of twin primes include 3 and 5, 11 and 13, 59 and 61, 71 and 73, 10 006 427 and 10 006 429. In 1979, two primes each of 703 digits were discovered. The number of pairs of twin primes is reputed to be unlimited, although they are naturally less frequent as we go higher.

Write down some other twins (or couplets), less than 100.

Triples (k, k + 2, k+ 4). A set of three numbers where k, k + 2 and k + 4 are primes is called a triple. Examples are (5, 7, 11), (11, 13, 17), (41, 43, 47), (101, 103, 107). There is another triple with primes less than 30. Can you discover it?

Both Aristotle (born 384 BC in Stagira and died 322 BC at Eubœa), and Euclid (a Professor of Mathematics at the University of Alexandria around 300 BC) distinguished between prime numbers and composites.

Primes	Difference
2	
3	1
5	2
7	2
11	4
13	2
17	4
19	2

Continue this table, listing the primes less than 100 (there are twenty five) and beside them, work out the differences. You will see a special number pattern emerging.

If we find the reduced numbers of primes, some give results which are themselves prime!

e.g. $11 \rightarrow 1 + 1 = 2$

Circle all the *very* prime primes!

Look at these remarkable patterns of primes:
$$7, 37, 337, 3337, 33\,337, 333\,337, ...$$
Unfortunately the next one in the sequence is *not* prime. A composite, 3 333 337 has factors of 7, 31 and 15 361.

In 1971, an American, with the aid of a computer, discovered a prime with 6002 digits in it. Then, in May 1979, the largest known prime was discovered. It is $2^{44\,497} - 1$, which has 13 395 digits!

Check this pattern with a calculator.
$$2 + 1 = 3$$
$$(2 \times 3) + 1 = 7$$
$$(2 \times 3 \times 5) + 1 = 31$$
$$(2 \times 3 \times 5 \times 7) + 1 = 211$$
$$(2 \times 3 \times 5 \times 7 \times 11) + 1 = 2311$$
$$(2 \times 3 \times 5 .... 11 \times 13) + 1 = 30\,031$$
$$(2 \times 3 \times 5 .... 13 \times 17) + 1 = 510\,511$$
$$(2 \times 3 \times 5 .... 17 \times 19) + 1 = 9\,699\,691$$

Research Find out what you can about Mersenne primes.

Goldbach's conjecture

Christian Goldbach (1690 – 1764) was an eighteenth-century mathematician who carried out extensive correspondence with Leonard Euler on problems in number theory.

In 1742, he stated two propositions:
(a)   Every even number greater than four is the sum of two odd primes.
(b)   Every odd number (omitting 3, 5 and 7) is the sum of three odd primes.

Complete the following table to test his first proposition. Some are started for you. Note: Many have more than one solution. Can you find them all?

6 = 3 + 3	8 = 3 + 5	$10 = \begin{array}{l} 3 + 7 \\ 5 + 5 \end{array}$	12 = 5 + 7
$14 = \begin{array}{l} 3 + 11 \\ 7 + 7 \end{array}$	$16 = \begin{array}{l} 3 + 13 \\ 5 + 11 \end{array}$	$18 = \begin{array}{l} 5 + 13 \\ 7 + 11 \end{array}$	20 =
22 =	24 =	26 =	28 =
30 =	32 =	$34 = \begin{array}{l} 5 + 29 \quad 11 + 23 \\ 3 + 31 \quad 17 + 17 \\ 15 + 19 \end{array}$	36 =
38 =	40 =	42 =	44 =
46 =	48 =	50 =	52 =
54 =	56 =	58 =	60 =
62 =	64 =	66 =	68 =
70 =	72 =	74 =	76 =
78 =	80 =	82 =	84 =
86 =	88 =	90 =	92 =
94 =	96 =	98 =	100 =
102 =	104 =	106 =	108 =
110 =	112 =	114 =	116 =

Remember the primes: 2, 3, 5, 7, 11, 13, 17, 19, 23, 29, 31, 37, 41, 43, 47, 53, 59, 61, 67, 71, 73, 79, 83, 89, 97. His conjecture has been verified for numbers well over 100 000.

His second proposition may be verified like this:
$$9 = 3 + 3 + 3$$
$$11 = 3 + 3 + 5$$
$$19 = 3 + 5 + 11$$
$$25 = 3 + 5 + 17 \quad \text{or} \quad 7 + 7 + 11$$
$$39 = 7 + 13 + 19 \quad \text{or} \quad 13 + 13 + 13$$

See how many you can do.

This table shows the distribution of primes up to 1000.

Numbers from	1	100	200	300	400	500	600	700	800	900
to	100	200	300	400	500	600	700	800	900	1000
Number of primes	25	21	16	16	17	14	16	14	15	14

Chebyshev's theorem

The Russian mathematician Chebyshev (1821 – 1894) proved that between every integer (greater than 1) and its double, there is at least one prime, e.g. between 2 and its double, 4, is the prime number 3, between 4 and 8, the prime 7, etc.
Test his theorem by working out ten other exercises.
    With the exception of 2 (which is the only even prime), the primes can be arranged in 2 groups:
A : 5 13 17 29 37 41 ....
B : 3 7 11 19 23 31 ....
• Divide all the numbers in group A by 4. What is the remainder in each case?
• Divide all the numbers in group B by 4. What remains?
• The numbers in group A can be written as the sum of two squares e.g. $5 = 1^2 + 2^2$. Calculate the others.

Just for fun
Choose any prime number greater than 3.
• Square it. Add 14. Divide by 12. The remainder will always be 3.
• Square it. Add 12. Divide by 12. The remainder will always be 1.
• Square it. Add 17. Divide by 12. The remainder will always be 6.

Perfect numbers

What is the sum of the divisors of 6 (excluding 6)? Your answer should have been 6, the sum of 3, 2 and 1. In the same way, find the sum of the divisors of 28 (excluding 28) and 496 (excluding 496).
    These are the smallest perfect numbers. The ancient Greeks discovered some of them, including those already mentioned, as well as 8128. It took nearly one thousand four hundred more years until the fifth perfect number was discovered in 1460. Is it surprising? The number was 33 550 336! The sixth is 8 589 869 056 and the seventh 137 438 691 328.
    A perfect number n is one in which the sum of its proper divisors (including 1 and excluding n) is n itself.
    Euclid proved that if n is a perfect natural number that makes $(2^n - 1)$ a prime and n is prime, then $2^{n-1}(2^n - 1)$ is a perfect number. This formula only gives even perfect numbers. No odd ones exist under 10^{10}. In 1750 Euler proved Euclid's formula to be correct.

Example: When $n = 3$, $2^{n-1}(2^n - 1) = 2^{3-1}(2^3 - 1)$
$$= 2^2(8 - 1)$$
$$= 4(7)$$
$$= 28$$

Now substitute $n = 5$, 7 and 11 in the formula.

Numerologists have attributed special significance to the numbers 6 and 28 because God created the world in 6 days and 28 is the number of days it takes for the moon to circle the earth.

Seventeen perfect numbers were known in 1953. The twelfth one, of 37 digits, is $2\,658\,455\,991\,569\,831\,744\,654\,692\,615\,953\,842\,176$. The seventeenth has 1373 digits while the twenty-fourth has 12003!!

Up until now the twenty-fifth and largest computer-generated one is $(2^{21701} - 1) \times 2^{21700}$
All perfect numbers are the sum of consecutive powers of 2, i.e.,
$$6 = 2^1 + 2^2$$
$$28 = 2^2 + 2^3 + 2^4$$
$$496 = 2^4 + 2^5 + 2^6 + 2^7 + 2^8$$

Every perfect number (except 6) is the sum of consecutive *odd cubes*, beginning with 1.
$$28 = 1^3 + 3^3$$
$$496 = 1^3 + 3^3 + 5^3 + 7^3$$
$$8128 = 1^3 + 3^3 + 5^3 + 7^3 + 9^3 + 11^3 + 13^3 + 15^3$$

Other properties

- All perfect numbers known are even and end in 6 or 28 (preceded by an odd number).
- The sum of the reciprocals of all the divisors is 2.
  e.g. for 6, $1 + \frac{1}{2} + \frac{1}{3} + \frac{1}{6} = 2$
- All known perfect numbers, except 6, have reduced numbers (or digital roots) of 1.
  e.g. $496 \rightarrow 4 + 9 + 6$
  $$= 19$$
  $$\rightarrow 1 + 9$$
  $$= 10$$
  $$\rightarrow 1 + 0$$
  $$= 1$$

Test for 28 and 8128.

A number, N, such that the sum of its divisors is greater than N is called an *abundant number* (e.g. 12), while *deficient numbers* have a sum less than N. Can you think of some examples?

Amicable numbers

If the sum of the divisors of a number is equal to a second number and if the sum of the divisors of the second equals the first number, they are said to be *amicable* or friendly. The smallest pair is 220 and 284. Another relatively small pair is 1184 and 1210, which was discovered by a sixteen-year old Italian schoolboy in 1866.

220 — 1, 2, 4, 5, 10, 11, 20, 22, 44, 55, 110,   Total 284
284 — 1, 2, 4, 71, 142   Total 220

Later, 17296 and 18416 were recorded, followed by 66928 and 66992, then 142310 and 168730.

Such numbers were known to the Greeks about AD 320 more than five hundred years after the discovery of perfect numbers. During the Middle Ages, the Arabs investigated amicable numbers and in 1747 Euler published a list of sixty pairs. Over six hundred pairs are now known!

Activities with patterns

1. Number patterns

As was stated earlier, mathematics is the study of patterns. In this segment you will discover how simple tables follow this principle. Copy and complete the tables.

Patterns of powers

		Answer	Reduced Number			Answer	Reduced Number
2^1	=	2	22	3^1	=	3	3
2^2	=	4	4	3^2	=	9	9
2^3	=	8	8	3^3	=	27	9
2^4	=	16	7	3^4	=	81	9
2^5	=	32	5	3^5	=	243	....
2^6	=	64	1	3^6	=	729	....
2^7	=	128	....	3^7	=	2187	....
2^8	=	....	....	3^8	=	....	....
2^9	=	....	....	3^9	=	....	....
2^{10}	=	....	....	3^{10}	=	....	....

Tables

		Reduced Number				Reduced Number
$8 \times 1 =$	8	8	$19 \times 1 =$	19	1	
$8 \times 2 =$	16	7	$19 \times 2 =$	38	2	
$8 \times 3 =$	24	6	$19 \times 3 =$	57	3	
$8 \times 4 =$	32	5	$19 \times 4 =$	76	....	
$8 \times 5 =$	40	....	$19 \times 5 =$	95	....	
$8 \times 6 =$	....	....	$19 \times 6 =$	114	....	
.... =	....	....	$19 \times 7 =$	....	....	
.... =	....	....	.... =	....	....	
.... =	....	....	.... =	....	....	
.... =	....	....	.... =	....	....	

Copy and complete:

$99 \times 11 = 1\ 0\ 8\ 9$

$99 \times 22 = 2\ 1\ 7\ 8$

$99 \times 33 = 3\ 2\ 6\ 7$

$99 \times 44 = 4\ ....\ 5\ ....$

$99 \times 55 = 5\ 4\ ....\ ....$

$99 \times 66 = 6\ ....\ ....\ 4$

$99 \times 77 = ...\ 6\ ....\ ....$

$99 \times 88 = ...\ ....\ 1\ 2$

$99 \times 99 = 9\ 8\ 0\ 1 = (98 + 01)^2!$

What 5-digit number, when divided by 4, gives an answer that is the reverse of your original number?

- Divide 2521 by 1, 2, 3, 4, 5, 6, 7, 8, 9 and 10.
  Write down the remainder in each case. Is it consistent?
- What is the sum of 98, 87, 69, 49, 22, 54, 67, 76 and 83?
  Now reverse the order of the digits (98 becomes 89) and find the sum.

Copy and complete :

$$9109 \times 1 = \quad 9\,109$$
$$9109 \times 2 = 18\,218$$
$$9109 \times 3 = 2..3..7$$
$$9109 \times 4 = \text{.... ....}6$$
$$9109 \times 5 =$$
$$9109 \times 6 =$$
$$9109 \times 7 =$$
$$9109 \times 8 =$$
$$9109 \times 9 =$$

$$999\,999 \times 2 = ?$$
$$999\,999 \times 3 =$$
$$999\,999 \times 4 =$$
$$999\,999 \times 5 = \quad$$ Calculators would
$$999\,999 \times 6 = \quad$$ make checking easier.
$$999\,999 \times 7 =$$
$$999\,999 \times 8 =$$
$$999\,999 \times 9 =$$

Without using a calculator, complete :

$$7 \times 7 \quad =$$
$$67 \times 67 \quad = \quad 4\,489$$
$$667 \times 667 \quad = \quad 444\,889$$
$$6667 \times 6667 \quad = \quad \text{....}\,889$$
$$\text{....}\,7 \times 66667 = 4(444(488)889$$
$$\text{....}\,7 \times \text{........}7 = \quad \text{........}$$

$$1 \times 99 = \quad 99$$
$$2 \times 99 = \quad 198$$
$$3 \times 99 = \quad 29..$$
$$4 \times \text{....} = \quad ..96$$
$$5 \times \text{....} = \quad 4..5$$
$$.. \times 99 = \quad \text{......}$$
$$7 \times ..9 = \quad \text{......}$$
$$8 \times 9.. = \quad \text{......}$$
$$.. \times \text{....} = \quad \text{......}$$

2. A real problem

Anyone who likes to bowl knows that the pins are set up in four rows (1, 2, 3, 4) like this

○ ○ ○ ○

○ ○ ○

○ ○

○

Suppose a giant set was assembled, with twenty rows. How many pins would be needed?

3. Did you say googol?

Here are some differences beween the British and American systems for naming large numbers.

	British	American
10^3	1 thousand	1 thousand
10^6	1 million	1 million
10^9	1 thousand million	1 billion
10^{12}	1 billion (1 million^2)	1 trillion
10^{15}	1 thousand billion	1 quadrillion
10^{18}	1 trillion (1 million^3)	1 quintillion
10^{21}	1 thousand trillion	1 sextillion
10^{24}	1 quadrillion	1 septillion
10^{63}	–	1 vigintillion
10^{100}	1 googol	1 googol
10^{googol}	1 googolplex	1 googolplex

The name 'googol' was devised by Pasha, the nine-year old nephew of the mathematician Dr Edward Kasner.

Did you know?
- It is generally conceded that a liberal estimate of the number of grains of sand on all the beaches of the world would be one quadrillion (10^{24}).
- Sir Arthur Eddington considered that the number of all particles in our universe would be approximately 10^{79}.
- An estimate of the total human population of the earth since the time of the remote 'ape man' falls short of 10 billion.
- The human brain contains about 10^{10} cells called *neurons*.
- An estimate of the total of all the words ever printed would not exceed 10^{17}.

What is the largest number that can be written using only three digits?
You probably answered 999.
What about 9^{99} or 9^{9^9}?
The latter number is equal to $9^{387\,420\,489}$, which has 369 693 100 digits if written out in full.

Problem
How long would it take to count to one million if you counted once every second?

4. Calculating a person's age

Ask a person to indicate the columns in which his/her age appears. You will then be able to determine the age.

A	B	C	D	E	F
1	2	4	8	16	32
3	3	5	9	17	33
5	6	6	10	18	34
7	7	7	11	19	35
9	10	12	12	20	36
11	11	13	13	21	37
13	14	14	14	22	38
15	15	15	15	23	39
17	18	20	24	24	40
19	19	21	25	25	41
21	22	22	26	26	42
23	23	23	27	27	43
25	26	28	28	28	44
27	27	29	29	29	45
29	30	30	30	30	46
31	31	31	31	31	47
33	34	36	40	48	48
35	35	37	41	49	49
37	38	38	42	50	50
39	39	39	43	51	51
41	42	44	44	52	52
43	43	45	45	53	53
45	46	46	46	54	54
47	47	47	47	55	55
49	50	52	56	56	56
51	51	53	57	57	57
53	54	54	58	58	58
55	55	55	59	59	59
57	58	60	60	60	60
59	59	61	61	61	61
61	62	62	62	62	62
63	63	63	63	63	63

Look carefully at this array of numbers. You will notice many patterns – odd numbers and consecutive numbers to name just two. How do you calculate the person's age? The secret is to find the sum of the digits at the top of the named columns. Try it.

5. String cutting and related number patterns

Suppose a short piece of string crosses itself once.
How many regions are formed?
The answer is 2 – one inside and one outside.

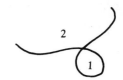

If it crosses twice, how many regions are there now?

Estimate the number of regions with 3 crosses.

Now imagine that you have a piece of string approximately 30 cm long. Given a certain number of cuts, calculate the number of pieces of string.

NUMBER OF CUTS (n)	0	1	2	3	4	5
NUMBER OF PIECES	1	2	3	4	....	....

Result : $(n + 1)$ pieces from n cuts.

Now fold the string *once* and complete the table :

NUMBER OF CUTS (n)	0	1	2	3	4	5
NUMBER OF PIECES	1	3	5	7	....	....

Result : $(2n + 1)$ pieces from n cuts.

Fold the string in the following ways before compiling tables and working out the number pattern and general term.

(a)

(c)

(b)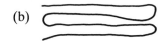

This time, *loop* the string around one arm of the scissors, before cutting.

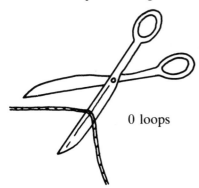

0 loops

NUMBER OF LOOPS (n)	0	1	2	3	4	5
NUMBER OF PIECES	2	3	4	5	....	....

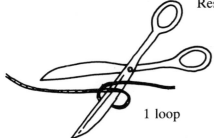

1 loop

Result : $(n + 2)$ pieces from n loops.

Now tie the ends of the string together and loop around the scissors.

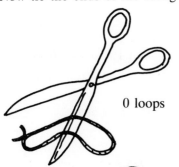

0 loops

NUMBER OF LOOPS (n)	0	1	2	3	4	5
NUMBER OF PIECES	2	4	6	8	....	....

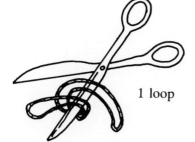

1 loop

Result : $(2n + 2)$ pieces from n loops.

Activity
How many pieces will be formed if the string is folded in each of these ways before being looped around the scissors? Give answers for 0, 1, 2, 3 loops. Verify by cutting, then predict for n loops.

(a)  (b)  (c)

Similar practical work, generating number patterns (and therefore formulae) could be devised using *circle* work. Find the maximum number of regions possible (in the circle) for varying numbers of:

(a) Radii   (b) Diameters

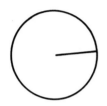

Radii	Regions
1	1
2	2
3	3
4	4
5	5

Diameters	Regions
1	2
2	4
3	6
4	8
5	10

n regions for n radii.

$2n$ regions for n diameters.

(c) Chords   (d) Tangents

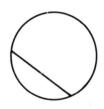

Chords	Regions
1	2
2	4
3	7
4	11
5	16

Tangents	Regions
1	2
2	6
3	10
4	15
5	21

Chords intersect one another
$\dfrac{n(n + 1)}{2} + 1$ regions for n chords.

$\dfrac{(n + 1)(n + 2)}{2}$ for n tangents.

(e) Secants   (f) Concentric Circles

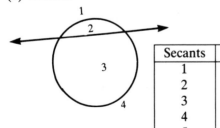

Secants	Regions
1	4
2	8
3	13
4	19
5	25

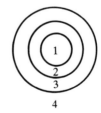

Circles	Regions
2	3
3	4
4	5
5	6
6	7

$n + 1$ regions for n circles.

$\dfrac{(n + 2)(n + 3)}{2} - 2$ regions for n secants.

Draw a circle. Mark any two points on the circumference. Join them. How many interior *regions* are formed? The answer is two.

Now put three points on another circle. Check that there are four regions.

Join four points to each other. Number?
Continue with 5, 6, 7 and 8 points, then complete a table:

No. of points	No. of areas
2	2
3	4
4	
5	
6	
7	
8	

Is there a pattern?

6. Polygon patterns

Draw the maximum number of diagonals in each polygon.

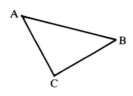

Triangle

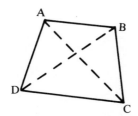

Quadrilateral

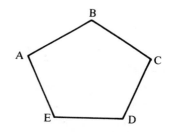

Pentagon

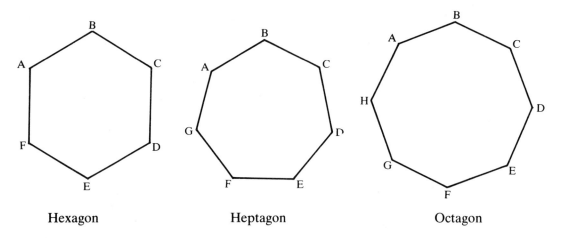

	Hexagon	Heptagon	Octagon

Now fill in this table.

Polygon	Number of vertices (V)	Number of diagonals from each vertex (N)										Number of diagonals (T)
		A	B	C	D	E	F	G	H	I	J	
Triangle	3	0	0	0	0	0	0	0	0	0	0	0
Quadrilateral	4	1	1	0	0							2
Pentagon	5	2	2	1	0							5
Hexagon	6			2								9
Heptagon			4									14
Octagon		5						1	0			
Nonagon												
Decagon	10											35
		★										

★ All numbers in column A should be three less than the number of vertices.

★ Note $T = \dfrac{V \times A}{2}$

$\qquad = \dfrac{n(n-3)}{2}$

* *Why are beehive cells hexagonal?*
Hint: Investigate the areas of an equilateral triangle, square, hexagon and circle, each having the same fixed perimeter of 6 units. Which has the greater space or area?

What is the maximum number of squares that can be drawn on these patterns of dots, without lifting your pencil off the paper? You may go horizontally and vertically only and may not go over a line.

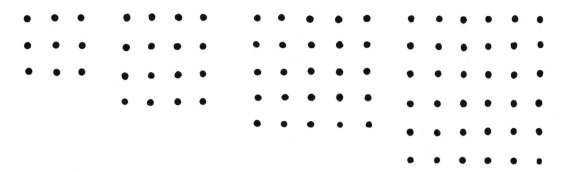

Maximum ....   Maximum ....   Maximum ....   Maximum ....

Using your answers as a guide, can you predict how many would be in the next two grid patterns?

  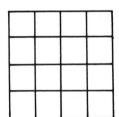 

How many squares (maximum) in each of these diagrams? When you have worked out your answers, see if they agree with these calculations:

$1^2 + 2^2$ $1^2 + 2^2 + 3^2$ $1^2 + 2^2 + 3^2 + 4^2$ $1^2 + 2^2 + 3^2 + 4^2 + 5^2$

= ....

7. Cyclic numbers

* Multiply 526 315 789 473 684 210 by any integer and all these numbers will appear, in cyclic order, in your answer.
* Use your calculator to work out:

$\frac{1}{7}$

$\frac{2}{7} =$

$\frac{3}{7} =$

$\frac{4}{7} = .\overline{571428}$

$\frac{5}{7} =$

$\frac{6}{7} =$

$\frac{1}{14} = .0\overline{714285}$

$\frac{3}{14} =$

$\frac{5}{14} =$

$\frac{5}{14} =$

$\frac{7}{14} =$

$\frac{9}{14} =$

$\frac{11}{14} =$

$\frac{13}{14} =$

Look for patterns!

$$\frac{1}{37} =$$ $$\frac{1}{13} =$$

$$\frac{2}{37} =$$ $$\frac{2}{13} =$$

$$\frac{3}{37} =$$ $$\frac{3}{13} =$$

$$\frac{4}{37} =$$ $$\frac{4}{13} =$$

$$\frac{5}{37} =$$ $$\frac{5}{13} =$$

$$\frac{6}{37} =$$

$$\frac{7}{37} =$$

8. Calculator patterns

The correct answers form a pattern of digits

- $11 \times (101^2)$ $=$
- $11^2 \times 101^2$ $=$
- $11^2 \times 24^2$ $=$
- $33^2 \times 30497$ $=$
- $273 \times 11^2 \times 37$ $=$
- $3^2 \times 37^2$ $=$
- $35^2 \times 47$ $=$
- 37×24^2 $=$
- $23^2 \times 418$ $=$
- 53×22^2 $=$
- $11^2 \times 28383$ $=$
- $24^2 \times 407$ $=$
- $77^2 \times 13^2$ $=$
- $21^2 \times 13^2 \times 407$ $=$
- $10\,067 \times 11^2 \times 3$ $=$

- 12×44^2 $=$
- $88^2 \times 23 \times 499$ $=$
- 6×24^2 $=$
- 3365×41^2 $=$
- $3 \times 11^2 \times 3401$ $=$
- $41 \times 27^2 \times 190$ $=$
- $73^2 \times 137$ $=$
- $154 \times 23^2 \times 247$ $=$
- $33 \times 91^2 \times 37$ $=$
- $143^2 \times 196$ $=$
- $7^2 \times 11^2 \times 13^2$ $=$
- $5^2 \times 457^2$ $=$
- $22^2 \times 303 \times 463$ $=$
- $3^2 \times 7^2 \times 11 \times 13^2 \times 37 =$

$$101 \times 1 =$$
$$101 \times 101 =$$
$$101 \times 101 \times 101 =$$
$$101 \times 101 \times 101 \times 101 =$$
$$101 \times 101 \times 101 \times 101 \times 101 =$$

$56 \div 11$	$=$		101×22	$=$
$78 \div 11$	$=$		101×222	$=$
$34 \div 11$	$=$		101×2222	$=$
$122 \div 11$	$=$		$101 \times 22\,222$	$=$
$89 \div 11$	$=$			
$37 \div 11$	$=$		101×33	$=$
$49 \div 11$	$=$		101×333	$=$
$60 \div 11$	$=$		101×3333	$=$
$50 \div 11$	$=$		$101 \times 33\,333$	$=$
$40 \div 11$	$=$			
$30 \div 11$	$=$		Need any checking?	

Use the calculator to do these patterns :

$1 \times 9 + 2 =$		$131 \times 11 \quad =$
$12 \times 9 + 3 =$		$131 \times 111 \quad =$
$123 \times 9 + 4 =$		$131 \times 1111 \quad =$
$1234 \times 9 + 5 =$		$131 \times 11\,111 \ =$
$12345 \times 9 + 6 =$		$131 \times 111\,111 =$

$$2^2 - 1 \times 3 =$$
$$3^2 - 2 \times 4 =$$
$$4^2 - 3 \times 5 =$$
$$5^2 - 4 \times 6 =$$
$$6^2 - 5 \times 7 =$$

$2 \times 5 \times 7^2 \times 233 \times 353 =$
Notice anything ?

Find answers to these :

a) $(1.618034)^2 - 1 =$

b) $1.618034 \times 0.618034 =$

c) $(1 + 1.618034) \times (1 - 0.618034) =$

d) $(1 + 1.618034) \times (0.618034) =$

e) $\dfrac{1}{1.618034} =$

f) $\dfrac{(1.618034)^4 - 2}{3} =$

Complete :

$9 \times 9 + 7 =$	$1 \times 9999 =$
$98 \times 9 + 6 =$	$2 \times 9999 =$
$987 \times 9 + 5 =$	$3 \times 9999 =$
$9876 \times 9 + 4 =$	$4 \times 9999 =$
$98765 \times 9 + 3 =$	$5 \times 9999 =$
$987654 \times 9 + 2 =$	$6 \times 9999 =$
$9876543 \times 9 + 1 =$	$7 \times 9999 =$
$98765432 \times 9 + 0 =$	$8 \times 9999 =$
	$9 \times 9999 =$

Chronological Table

BC

circa 2000 — • Babylonians use π as $3\frac{1}{8}$

• Egyptians use π as $\left(\frac{16}{9}\right)^2$ or 3.1605.

12th century — • Chinese use $\pi = 3$

circa 550 — • Bible (I Kings vii,23) implies $\pi = 3$

3rd century — • Archimedes establishes $3\frac{10}{71} < \pi < 3\frac{1}{7}$ and $\pi = \frac{211875}{67441} = 3.14163$

AD

2nd century — • Ptolemy uses $\pi = \frac{377}{120}$ or 3.14166....

3rd century — • Chung Hung → $\pi = \sqrt{10} = 3.16....$

5th century — • Tsu Chung-Chi says $3.1415926 < \pi < 3.1415927$

1220 — • Fibonacci finds $\pi \approx 3.141818$

1583 — • Simon Duchesne finds $\pi = \left(-\frac{39}{22}\right)^2 = 3.14256....$

1593 — • Van Roomen finds π to 15 decimal places

1665 – 1666 — • Newton discovers calculus and calculates pi to over 16 decimal places.

1705 — • Sharp calculates π to 72 decimal places.

1719 — • de Lagney calculates 127 places

1794 — • Vega calculates 140 places

1844 — • Dase calculates 200 places

1855 — • Richter calculates 500 places

1873 – 74 — • Shanks calculates 707 places

1946 — • Ferguson calculates 620 places

1947 — • Ferguson calculates 808 places using a desk calculator

1949 — • Computer ENIAC programmed to compute 2037 places

42

1954 – 55	● N.O.R.C. programmed to compute 3089 decimals
1957	● PEGASUS (London) computes 7480 decimals
1959	● IBM (Paris) computes 7480 decimals
1961	● IBM (N.Y.) computes 100 000 places
1966	● IBM (Paris) computes 250 000 places
1967	● CDC (Paris) computes $\frac{1}{2}$ million places

$\pi \approx 3.14159265358979323846264338327950288419716939937510582097494459230781640628620899$

● Starting with the 710 150th decimal digit, there is a run of 7 consecutive 3s i.e. ....353733333338638....

● The first digit of π is the first perfect number (if 1 can be considered perfect), the sum of the first three digits (141) is the second perfect number, the sum of the first seven digits equals the third perfect number.

● *Guinness Book of Records*: On 15 Oct.1974, Michael Poulteney memorised π correctly to 3025 decimals – it took twenty five minutes to write these decimals out!!!

9. Patterns to peruse

Flipping cubes

A cube can occupy a space in twenty-four different ways. Fill in the missing letters:

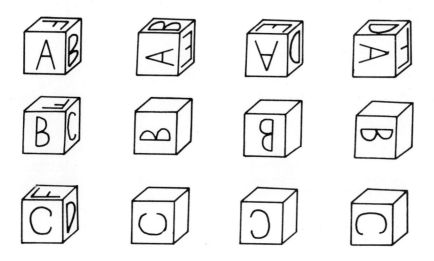

UNIT 2

DESIGNS OF OUR TIMES

The mathematician's patterns, like the painter's or poet's, must be beautiful; the ideas, like the colours or the words, must fit together in a harmonious way ..... There is no permanent place in the world for ugly maths.

G.H. Hardy

The study of design can be most rewarding for students. Geometric design is all around us. Consider the regular and semi-regular tessellations in wall and floor tiles, wallpaper patterns and the use of mathematical shapes in fabric designs, stained glass windows, iron work and wood carving.

Transformation geometry can be used as a tool for analysing Maurits Escher's drawings or even for designing new Escher-type creations. A transformation is a correspondence or matching between points on a plane. We usually concentrate on three transformations:

1. Translations   (slides)
2. Rotations   (turns)
3. Reflections   (flips)

Shears and dilations (enlargements) are also transformations. (Shears are alterations to a shape brought about by the movement of sides on an unaltered base line, a square changing to a rhombus.)

Investigations have led to the classification of translation, rotation and reflection as isometries because they preserve distance. ('Isometry' is derived from two Greek words meaning equal measure.)

Thus we can say that one congruent figure can be mapped onto another by either a translation or a rotation (which are both direct isometries), or by a reflection, or a combination of a translation and a reflection (which are opposite isometries). A combination of a translation and a reflection (or a half-turn and a reflection) is sometimes called a *glide reflection*.

In analysing designs, reference is often made to the seventeen groups of two-dimensional crystallography that were determined in 1891. Ten of these may be used if the shape of the basic unit containing the motif is a square (see asterisks).

This table outlines those seventeen groups:

Symbol	Generators
* p1	Two translations
* p2	Three half turns
* pm	Two reflections and a translation
* pg	Two parallel glide reflections
* cm	A reflection and a parallel glide reflection
* pmm	Reflections in the four sides of a rectangle
* pmg	A reflection and two half turns
* pgg	Two perpendicular glide reflections
* cmm	Two perpendicular reflections and a half turn
* p4	A half turn and a quarter turn
p4m	Reflections in the three sides of a (45°, 45°, 90°) triangle
p4g	A reflection and a quarter turn
p3	Two rotations through 120°
p3m1	A reflection and a rotation through 120°
p31m	Reflections in the three sides of an equilateral triangle
p6	A half turn and a rotation through 120°
p6m	Reflections in the three sides of a (30°, 60°, 90°) triangle

Careful analysis of everyday patterns reveals that one or more isometries are commonly used. Take, for instance, the blocks that are available commercially for building decorative walls, fences or screens. They are usually square or rectangular in shape.

There are four very common square blocks that preserve line symmetry, i.e. they have four axes of symmetry. This distinctly limits the design when they are laid. In fact, if they are translated, rotated or reflected, the finished effect is identical as they are unaltered by these transformations.

Being square they tessellate perfectly.

Note: As they each have a uniform vertical cross-section, they are considered to be *two-dimensional* pattern formations.

On 1 cm grid paper, copy and complete the 4×4 square according to the congruence transformations indicated. Use colour and draw the motif as accurately as possible, for a very dramatic effect.

 Translate

 Rotate

 Reflect

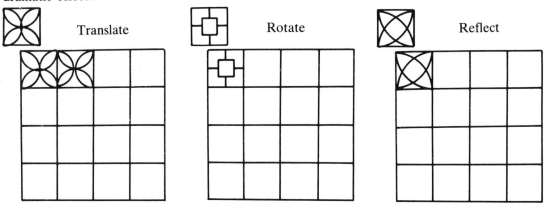

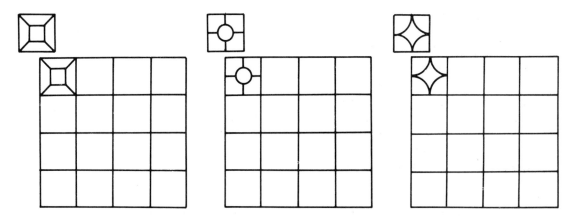

Many interesting patterns can be made from asymmetrical blocks. There are at least eight types available. Collecting photos or slides of these types could be an interesting class project.

Try the following designs based on the unit given. The actual *number* of different designs for any one motif will vary from as few as two to as many as nineteen!

Investigate all the different designs from only *one* motif. They are started for you.

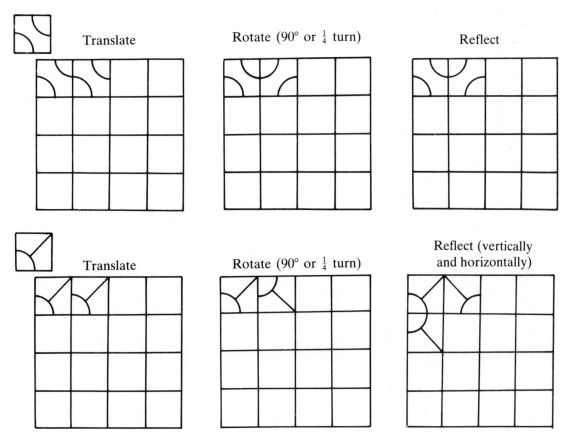

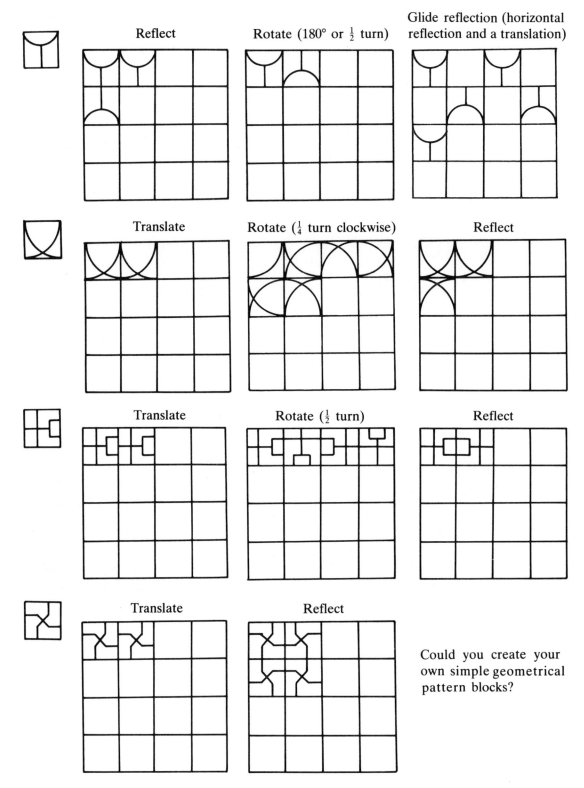

Reflect Rotate (180° or ½ turn) Glide reflection (horizontal reflection and a translation)

Translate Rotate (¼ turn clockwise) Reflect

Translate Rotate (½ turn) Reflect

Translate Reflect

Could you create your own simple geometrical pattern blocks?

48

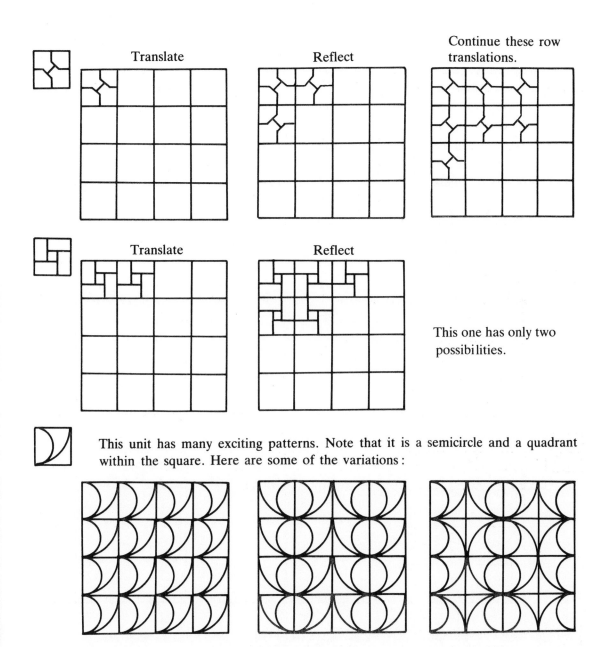

Translate

Reflect

Continue these row translations.

Translate

Reflect

This one has only two possibilities.

This unit has many exciting patterns. Note that it is a semicircle and a quadrant within the square. Here are some of the variations:

49

Can you distinguish the transformations that have occurred?

Varied dramatic effects can be
achieved by simple colouring.
These 4 designs have the same
basic outline.

Rectangular blocks are also plentiful. See how many different types you can find. Here are
some to get you started:

 This 'block' can be arranged in two distinctly different
patterns.

Keep a record of the different arrangements. Try to analyse the transformations and investigate
to see how many *more* patterns can be made. Some will be line symmetrical; others will have
rotational symmetry while others will be asymmetrical.
 Colour some of your finished patterns to give an interesting visual effect.

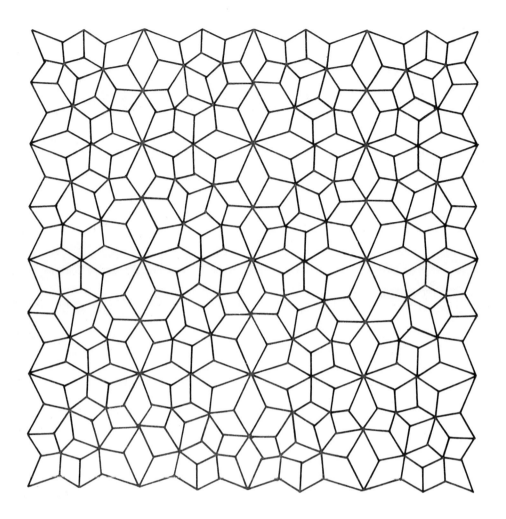

This pattern, based on polygons, has many exciting effects when enlarged with a pantograph and coloured in no more than three toning colours. Perhaps a class competition could be arranged to see who could create the most dramatic optical illusion.

UNIT 3

THE PATTERNS OF LIFE

....in the air
A thousand streamers floated fair
Various in shape, device and hue,
Green, sanguine, purple, red and blue,
Broad, narrow, swallow-tailed and square

Sir Walter Scott, *Marmion*

Flags are used as an ensign, standard or signal, or for display, ceremonial and decorative purposes. Symbolic standards were used by the Egyptians, Assyrians and Jews. These were usually poles with a metal image of a bird, animal or some object on the top. Biblical references to flags are also numerous. Even early hunters and warriors needed identification so early flags were probably made of animal skins or feathers of some kind.

It is believed that the ancient Chinese and East Indians made the first *cloth* flags as long ago as 1100 BC!

The oldest national flag still in use is the *Dannebrog* (meaning Strength of Denmark) which is a red ensign, dovetailed, bearing a white cross. Its design is over seven hundred years old; legend has it that it originated in 1219.

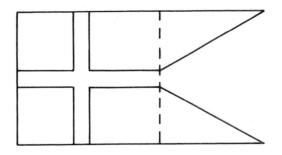

The Dannebrog provides opportunites for calculations:
(a) The squares have sides $\frac{3}{7}$ of the hoist.
(b) Rectangles by the fly have a length $\frac{5}{4}$ of their width.
(c) Swallow tails have a length $1\frac{1}{2}$ times as great as that of the fly rectangles.

The historical significance of flags is well known – for example, they may represent and inspire courage, spirit in the midst of disaster, defiance of the enemy and the ideals of the nation. For example, the Crusaders carried flags in their religious wars.

In Europe, the heraldic flags of the Middle Ages were different from today's flags. They were usually square or rectangular with the size depending on the owner's rank. Most were called banners and told, in visual form, the history and victories of the family or clan. (Look up the Royal Standard or the Standard of George I.)

The earliest book on flags was compiled by a monk. Entitled *The Book of all the Knowledge of all the Kingdoms, Lords and Lordships in the World*, it described the travels of a Catalan Franciscan monk who lived in the fourteenth century. His name is unknown!

In June 1966, the American flag was carried to the moon, sealed in the structure of Surveyor I. It was unfurled when the crew of Apollo XI landed on 20 July 1969. On the plaque left behind were inscribed the words:

'*We came in peace, for all mankind.*'

The flags of the Soviet Union and the United States have now been placed on the moon's surface, and sent to the planet Venus and past Jupiter.

An excellent source of work on measurement, design and accurate constructions, flags can also be used for research assignments. Quite a number of national flags are geometrical in composition.

The following characteristics can be investigated:
1. The size and proportions (length to width).
2. The colour scheme used.
3. The geometry of the design.

1. Size and proportion

Most flags used on land are in the ratio of 5:3, while those used at sea are in the ratio 2:1. A flag is generally divided into four sections, signifying the order of heraldic importance. Many naval ensigns contain a flag within a flag!

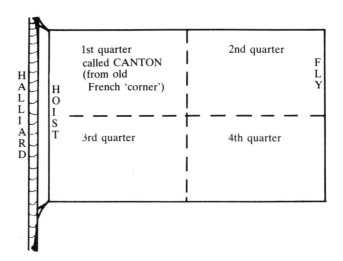

Obviously the rectangle is the most common shape nowadays. The flags of Switzerland and the Vatican City are the only square national flags (ratio 1:1). No country has a triangular flag.

Proportions of some well-known flags include 2:1, 15:13, 7:4, 12:7 and 7:6.

2. Colour

British heraldry uses only five colours; blue, red, black, green and purple. Overseas, orange is also included. Yellow and white are *not* regarded as colours, but as 'metals .... *or* (gold) and *argent* (silver)' (from *The Book of Flags*, G.Campbell and I.D.Evans, OUP). One of the strict rules of heraldry is that a colour must not be placed on a colour, nor a metal on a metal. No two colours must touch, but must be separated by a narrow band of yellow or white (look at the Union Jack). Today, many modern flags disregard this rule.

Bold bands of contrasting colours, either vertical or horizontal, are the most easily distinguished. Outside Scandinavia, many European countries fly tricolour flags. Most conform with the heraldic rule by having a white or yellow stripe between two colours.

The tricolour of France is comparatively recent in design. The three vertical stripes differ slightly in width, although they at first appear equal. From the hoist (the part nearest the mast), the stripes of blue, white and red are in the ratio 30:33:37.

Examples with vertical stripes:

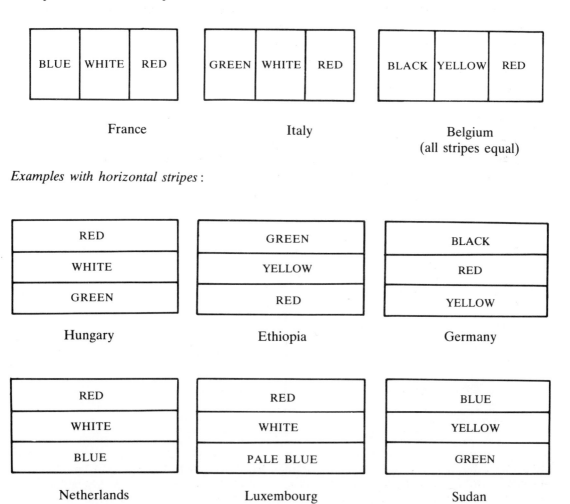

France	Italy	Belgium
		(all stripes equal)

Examples with horizontal stripes:

Hungary

Ethiopia

Germany

Netherlands

Luxembourg

Sudan

3. Design

As well as stripes, numerous flags contain an emblem or motif. Find pictures of the flags of India and Lebanon. What has been added?

Flags containing crosses are common. It may seem strange that war flags should bear a cross, a Christian symbol of peace. Throughout history, peace-loving men and women have had to fight in self-defence and to uphold their ideals.

Emperor Constantine, who ruled a large part of Europe in the fourth century AD, is said to have had a vision in which he saw a cross in the sky, bearing the words '*in this sign conquer*'. He adopted the cross as the sign of his army, fought and won, and established Christianity as the religion of his empire.

The Scandinavian countries have very similar flags. Countries which are related, or which have had a very similar history, are often akin in ideals and usually express them by flying the same kind of flag.

In Denmark, Norway (flag dimensions 11:8), Iceland, Sweden and Finland, the centre of the cross is not in the centre of the flag but nearer the hoist. See the similarities!

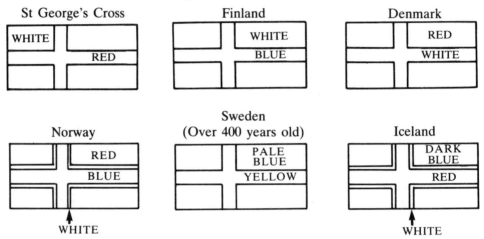

The Greek cross (with equal arms) dates from the fourteenth century and appears on a red background on the flag of Switzerland.

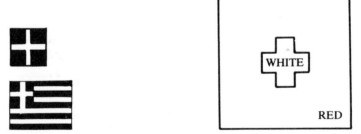

Somewhat similar is the Red Cross emblem, with the red cross signifying danger, on a square white background. One fifth of the flag is white. Make a sketch of it.

Find out the features of the Tongan flag.

The St Andrews cross was known when this symbol was used by Leibniz in seventeenth-century Germany. He found ✕ too similar to the algebraic 'unknown *x*', however.

The use of stars on national flags is widespread, with most having five, six or seven vertices.

Can you draw an accurate six-pointed star within a circle?

A pentagram or five-pointed star is the ancient symbol of authority. It occurs on the flags of Morocco, Ghana, Chile, Cuba, Burma, Liberia and Yugoslavia.

Morocco

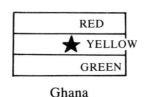

Ghana

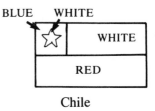

Chile

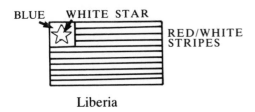

Cuba

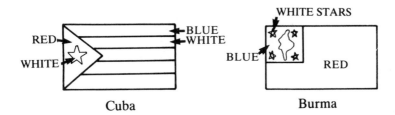

Burma

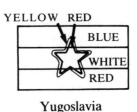

Liberia

Yugoslavia

Construction to make a perfect pentagram

1. Take a rectangular piece of paper approximately 26 cm × 20 cm.
2. Fold along axis A (folded edge on R.H.S.). (Figure 1)
3. Take bottom right-hand corner A, and bring it up to the midpoint of top edge (C). Crease DF. (Figures 2 and 3)
4. Bring DF up so that it lies along edge AF. Crease. (Figure 4)
5. Take E and fold it underneath, along edge DF, (Figure 5)
6. With scissors, cut along line indicated in Figure 6.

Unfold star.

Variations: Try cuts indicated in Figures 7 and 8. Did you make a regular pentagram or a regular decagon?

FIGURE 1

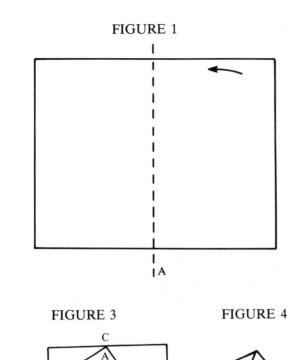

FIGURE 2

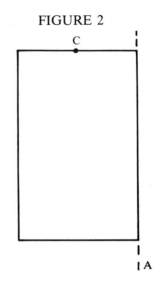

FIGURE 3

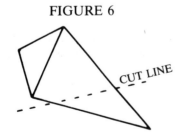

FIGURE 4

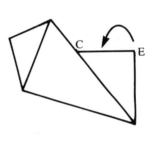

FIGURE 5

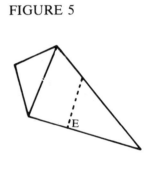

FIGURE 6

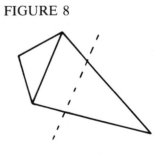

CUT LINE

FIGURE 7

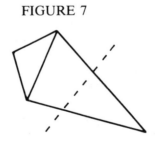

FIGURE 8

A six-pointed star appears on the flag of Israel. An ancient religious symbol comprising two interlaced triangles, it is known as the Star of David.

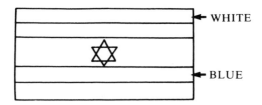

Circles

These appear on the Japanese flag and that of Bangladesh.

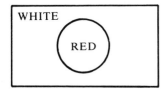 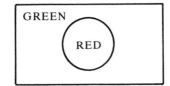

Ratio 5 : 3
Diameter equal
to $\frac{2}{3}$ width

Concentric circles of red, white and dark blue appear on the flag of the Royal Air Force. A variation of the circle motif, the monad, is found on South Korea's flag. The monad ('one', a unit of being) is an ancient emblem that divides the circle into two equal halves. It has mystical significance.

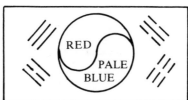

Special Flags

(a) The Olympic flag has five interlaced rings, each of a different colour on a white background. The chain, an ancient symbol of unity and cooperation was intended to represent the five continents of the world linked in unbroken friendship.

Blue represents Europe, black–Africa, red–Australasia, yellow–Asia, green–America.

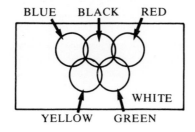

(b) The Isle of Man flag has a red background with three white-and-yellow legs, united at the thigh. Called the *Trinacria*, it is supposedly based on an ancient emblem of Sicily.

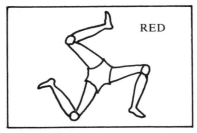

(c) In the fourteenth century, the Royal Navy devised flag signals. A flag half way up the mast called the captains into council, hoisted to the masthead it gave the warning *enemy in sight*. By the seventeenth century, flags, including the national emblems, conveyed meanings by their positions.

The first real flag code was compiled in the eighteenth century. Each flag represented a number from 0 to 9. Special flags indicated 'yes' or 'no'.

By using flags singly, in pairs or triples, a large number of different messages could be conveyed. A code book explained the combinations. A ten flag code like this enabled Nelson to give his famous signal at Trafalgar. Here are the flags he used:

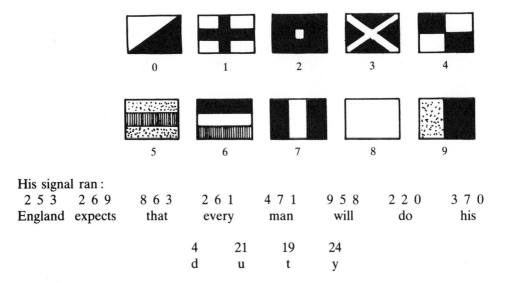

His signal ran:

2 5 3	2 6 9	8 6 3	2 6 1	4 7 1	9 5 8	2 2 0	3 7 0
England	expects	that	every	man	will	do	his

4	21	19	24
d	u	t	y

(The word 'duty' had to be spelt separately as it did not appear in the code book!)

Many airlines have their own house flags which may be flown on aircraft, over airfields, on office buildings and in civil processions. For example, Australia has a flying kangaroo on the Qantas flag; Air Canada uses a red flag bearing the maple leaf and Air France combines the emblem of Pegasus, the flying horse, with a modified tricolour of blue, white and red.

Shipping lines also have their own flags. Investigate some of their designs.

UNIT 4

EXPERIMENTS WITH PATTERNS

THE BEAUTY AND FASCINATION OF PATTERNS

The essence of Mathematics is its freedom.

Georg Cantor (1845 – 1918)

There are only 5 regular convex solids with congruent faces and congruent interior angles at the corners – the regular tetrahedron, hexahedron (cube), octahedron, dodecahedron and icosohedron. The ancient Pythagoreans studied them, associating the solids with the four elements of fire, earth, air and water. The dodecahedron was the one associated with the universe.

Plato (429 – 348 BC) in his *Timaeus* also wrote about the connection. Hence the solids became known as Platonic solids. Both Euclid (c.300 BC) and Kepler (1571 – 1630) included sections on polyhedra in their works. It is probable that the Greeks knew that a sphere could be drawn around any one of these figures, so that it touched every vertex.

The tetrahedron

The net of a regular tetrahedron is made of four congruent equilateral triangles.

Make a tetrahedron out of six straws of equal length. Wool can be threaded through the straws or pipecleaners bent at the vertices. Straws are readily available in a wide variety of colours. Spokes from an old umbrella make satisfactory 'needles'.

If the midpoint of each face is joined, the resulting 'skeleton' solid so formed is a smaller, similar tetrahedron!

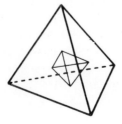

This means a tetrahedron is the dual of itself. This is called a self-dual.

In two dimensions, a square is its own dual.

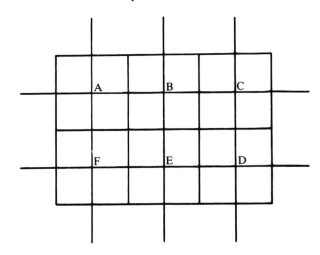

The centres of the original tessellating squares (A, B, C, D, E, and F) are joined. The connecting lines must bisect the edges at right angles.

A model of a tetrahedron can be made from any sealed envelope.

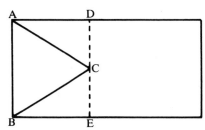

Draw an equilateral triangle on one side of one end of the envelope (length of side equals width of envelope). Cut along DE. Discard right hand side of envelope. Crease CA, CB. Bring points D and E together.

A sliced tetrahedron puzzle

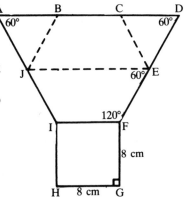

- Carefully make two nets, given these dimensions. Use thick cardboard.
- Score the dotted lines and tape the edges, to form two congruent solids.
- Put them together to form a tetrahedron.

The hexagon BCEFIJ, the square IFGH, and the triangles ABJ and CDE all have equal sides.

A more complicated puzzle

This puzzle is similar to the preceding one, though more difficult to solve. Make four identical models, each made from this net. Equal sides are marked.

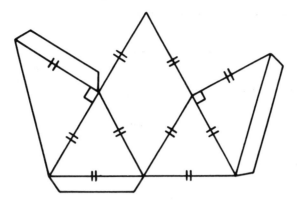

A two-dimensional triangular grid may be formed into an astonishing three-dimensional flexing 'ring' called an IsoAxis, invented by Wallace Walker. The form can be turned inside out or rotated through five transformations, before coming back to its original position.

This net is made of sixty connected isosceles right-angled triangles.

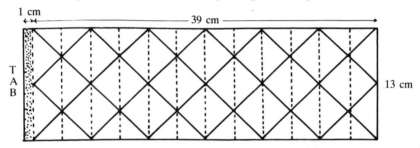

Fold away from you along the black lines, and towards you on the dotted ones. Glue or tape the ends together to form an 'open' cylinder. Indent (pleat or push in) the smaller triangles on both top and bottom edges. They form a valley.

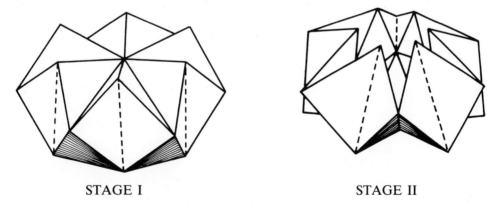

STAGE I   STAGE II

The remaining stages are left for you to discover!

63

Imagine that the grid is now distorted, or stretched horizontally, making all the angles 60°. When this is assembled a ring of tetrahedra is formed.

n tetrahedra, each joined to its neighbour by a pair of opposite edges to form a ring, will rotate if $n \geqslant 6$, and can be knotted if $n \geqslant 22$.

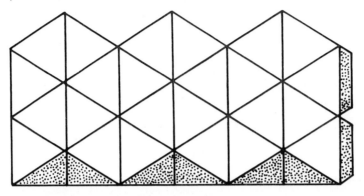

Crease all lines thoroughly and assemble to form a ring of six joined tetrahedra. They can be rotated through the centre in a continuous motion.

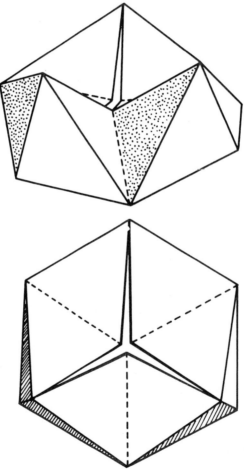

Bold geometric designs or different pictures or colours may be put on each view. There should be four different views in the cycle.

A rotating magic ring of eight tetrahedra

On a piece of cardboard at least 63 cm long, construct this net using a pair of compasses.

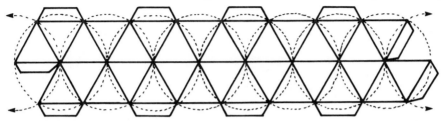

Carefully label the tabs and number the equilateral triangles. The triangles should have an edge of 7 cm.

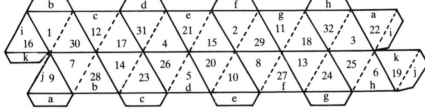

Cut out, then fold the dotted lines away from you and the black lines in the opposite direction. Crease thoroughly. Glue the tabs to their corresponding edges i.e. tab b to edge b, etc. The eight tetrahedra should come together in the centre and when flexed or rotated, should form an attractive model.

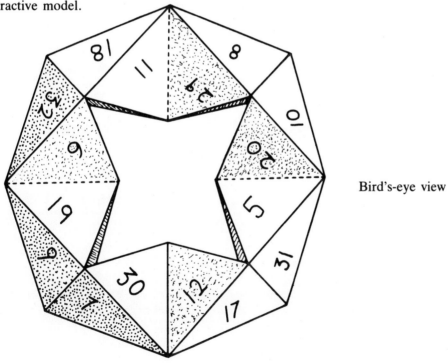

Bird's-eye view

This is a magic rotating ring with a magic number of 132. Instead of numbering, it may be coloured attractively.

What can you discover about the sum of the numbers on each tetrahedron?

The string of tetrahedra can be made longer by extending the net, though the ends will be joined differently. The figure made of ten pyramids is particularly attractive and its net is shown below:

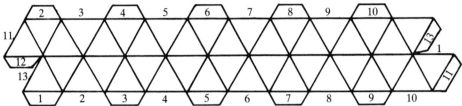

As before, join tab 2 to edge 2, 3 to 3, 4 to 4, etc. securely gluing each part. Continue until you stick tab 13 to edge 13, then bring the two ends together to form a ring. You should now be able to rotate the ring.

Flexagons .... Designs with a twist

Flexagons are figures made by folding square or isometric grid paper into a square or hexagon shape. The ends are joined in such a way that if the squares or equilateral triangles are coloured in a special way, the model can be continuously folded and unfolded (flexed) to produce different colours in turn.

Type A

These flexagons can be made using 2 cm square units.

Step 1   Cut out and number this hexomino (a shape formed by 6 squares).

Step 2   Reflect the shape. Number the back.

Step 3   With the back facing you, bend the tab back along line *a*.

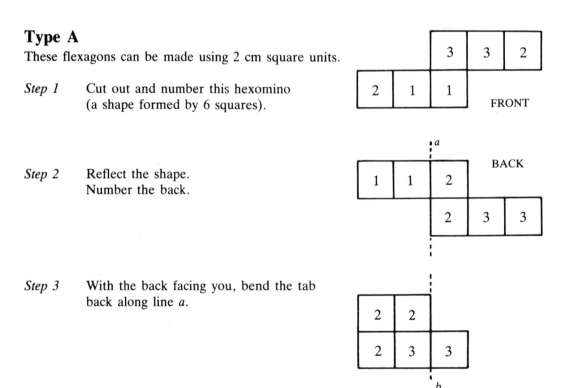

66

Step 4   Fold the ☐3 square towards you, along line *b*

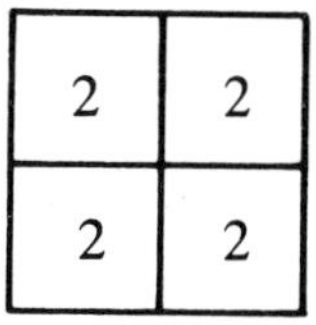

2	2
2	2

Step 5   Join the 2 edges with a piece of sticky tape.
Fold the flexagon backwards to open it ....

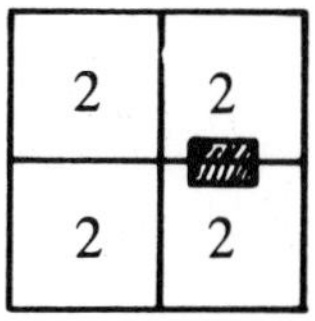

2	2
2	2

For a more complex flexagon, follow these steps:

Type B

Step 1   Cut out a 4 unit × 3 unit rectangle. Number.

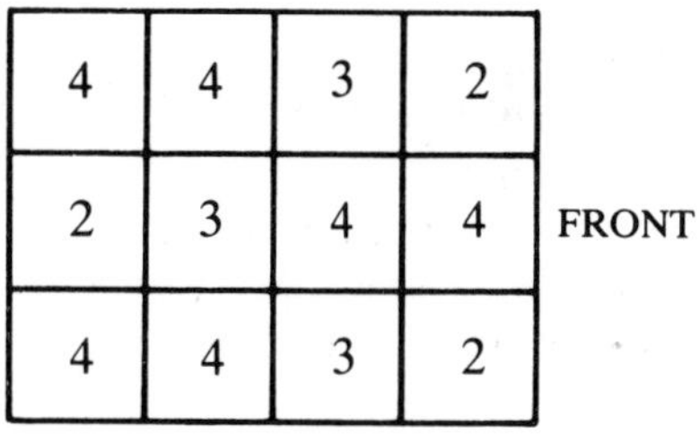

4	4	3	2
2	3	4	4
4	4	3	2

FRONT

Step 2   Turn the rectangle over and number the back.

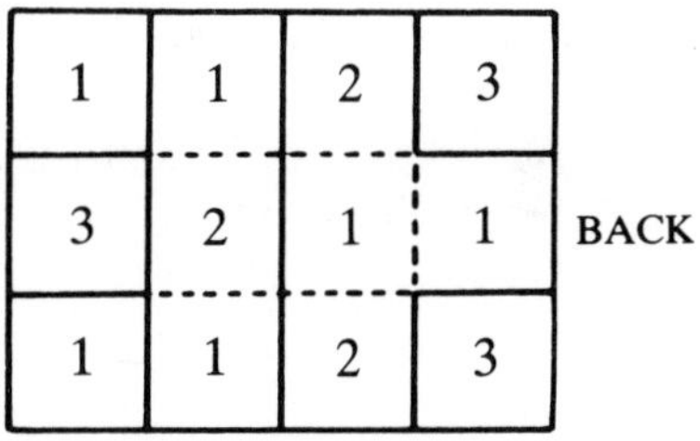

1	1	2	3
3	2	1	1
1	1	2	3

BACK

Cut round the dotted line and fold the centre piece away from you.

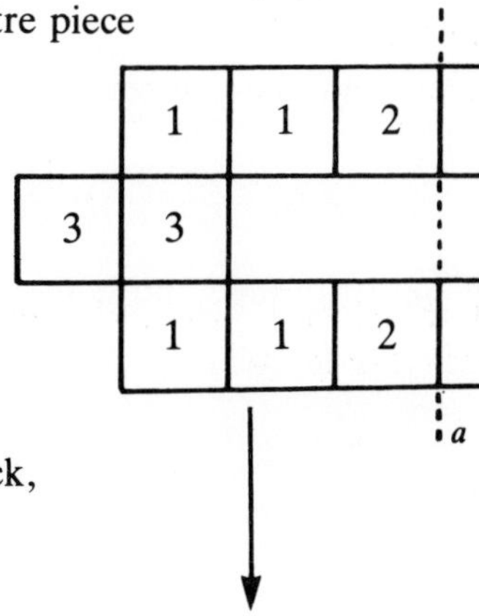

	1	1	2	3
3	3			1
	1	1	2	3

a

Step 3   Fold the right-hand column of squares back, about line *a*.

67

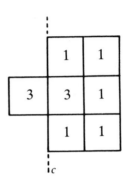

Step 4 Fold the column of twos back, about line *b* and fold the ③ towards you about line *c*.

Step 5 Complete the flexagon by joining the 2 edges with adhesive tape

Flex by bringing the ones face-to-face – open it from the back. How many sets of numbers flex up?

Another model is a more interesting variation as there are more sets of numbers in the cycle.

Type C

5	2	1	3	FRONT
1			2	
2			1	←— Cut here
3	1	2	5	

Step 1 Cut out this shape and number it.

Step 2   Turn it over and number the back.
Fold each square towards you to crease all lines.
Flatten out again.

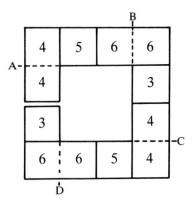

- At crease A fold the fours together – face-to-face.
- At crease B fold the top strip right over so that the two sixes face each other.
- At crease C fold the top strip upwards so that the fours are facing.
- At crease D fold the strip over so the sixes face each other. Your figure should look like this :

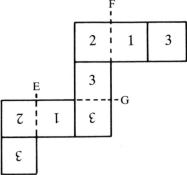

- At crease E fold the strip 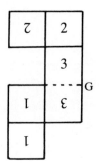 away from you to make :

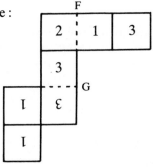

- At crease F fold the strip |1|3| back to make :

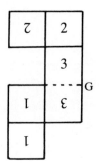

- At crease G fold the strip upwards

ε	I
	I

  and tuck the $\boxed{3}$ underneath the $\boxed{z}$.

z	2
2	z

- Attach adhesive tape (as shown).

Flex vertically and horizontally.

Hexaflexagons

Fascinating hexaflexagons were invented by Professor Arthur H. Stone, early in 1939, when he was a student in America. They have also been investigated by Bryant Tuckerman, Richard Feynman and John Tukey.

Hexaflexagons are polygons, folded from straight or crooked strips of paper or cardboard, which have the fascinating property of changing their faces when flexed.

There are various types of hexaflexagons, all based on joined equilateral triangles.

The hexaflexagon family is:

The Unahexa – Strips of 3 triangles, folded flat. The opposite ends are joined to make a Möbius strip with a triangular edge! It does not flex.

The Duahexa – A simple hexagon cut from a sheet of paper, it has 2 faces, but does not flex.

The Trihexa – This has only one form and is made up of a chain (or strip) of 10 equilateral triangles. The simplest flexing model, it has only 3 different 'faces'. See instructions later.

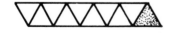

The Tetrahexa – There is only one form, folded from a crooked strip of 13 triangles.

70

The Pentahexa –

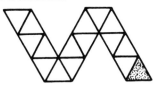

Again, this model, of 16 triangles, is folded from a crooked strip.

N.B. The shaded triangles are to glue at the end.

The Hexahexa –

The most popular hexaflexagon, this model can be made from 3 nets (one straight strip and two crooked strips).

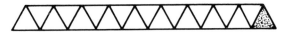

The first *hexa* in its name denotes that there are 6 faces, while the second *hexa* means that when folded, it is hexagonal in shape.

See instructions further on.

The Heptahexa –

This has four varieties.

Construction by paper folding

Cut long strips of paper 5 cm wide.

- Fold the strip in half, horizontally, on the left hand end only (CD). Undo paper.

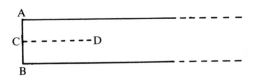

- Fold vertex B to fall on CD. Crease AE.
  What type of triangle is ABE?
  Fold so that crease EG forms along EB.

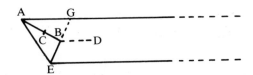

- Next, fold along GA, forming another triangle. Continue folding back and forth until 10 equilateral triangles have been formed.
  Cut off the excess strip as well as △ABE.

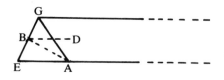

You are now ready to fold the strip to form a *trihexaflexagon*.

If preferred, thin cardboard will give a more lasting model. A geometrical construction lesson with instruments could precede the model making.

The trihexaflexagon

- Carefully mark the strip into 10 equilateral triangles.

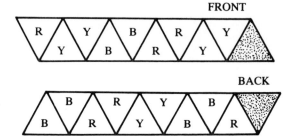

Colour triangles as shown.
R = red, Y = yellow, B = blue.

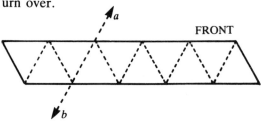

- Fold the strip backwards along line *ab*. Turn over.

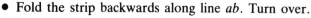

- Fold backwards along line *cd*.

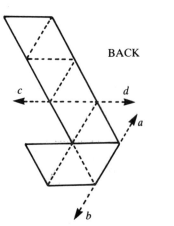

- Place second last triangle on top of the first i.e. flip it forward.

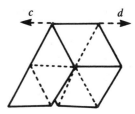

- Fold last triangle backwards and glue to the other side of the first triangle.

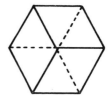

Flexing

To flex the model, two adjacent triangles are pinched together and the opposite vertex is pushed down with the crease pushed into the centre. This forms a three-winged 'fan'. Flex outwards at the vertex to reveal another face.

Continue until you complete the cycle.

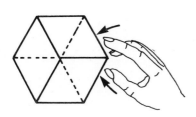

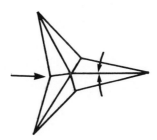

The hexahexaflexagon

- Carefully mark a strip of good paper or thin cardboard into 19 equilateral triangles, both front and back. An edge length of 6 cm is suitable. Number as shown. Leave the end one blank (as indicated). The triangles must coincide *exactly* on both back and front.

Instead of numbering, six different colours may be used.

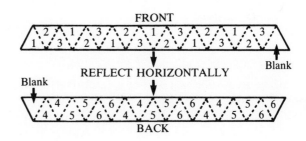

73

- With the back facing you, fold the strip so that 4 goes on 4, 5 on 5, 6 on 6, and so on.

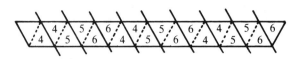

- The resulting folded strip is then folded back on line *ab*.

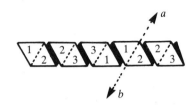

- Turn model over. Fold 'tail' back under, along line *cd*.

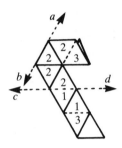

- This forms a hexagon with a flap.
  Flip the back triangle to the front to expose all the twos on one side. Fold the blank triangle onto the other one and glue securely.
  The reverse side of your hexahexaflexagon should have all ones. Fold carefully along the three axes of symmetry.

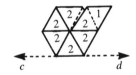

You are now ready to flex it. By pinching together any two adjacent triangles and gently opening up the hexagon at the centre, you should be able to reveal six sets of numbers.

Sometimes you may find it will not flex – just move to another pair of adjacent triangles. (The 'Tuckerman traverse'!)

A statistical phenomenon

By using your hexahexaflexagon, a statistical experiment can be carried out that reveals a surprising result.

Flex your model one hundred times and record the cycles of numbers. You may find that 6 (or 4) is very elusive, yet you know it is there. Continue patiently, trying to break the 'cycles'.

Your numbers could go like this:

```
1  2  3  1  2  3  1  2  3  1  2  3  1  2  5  1  2  5
1  2  5  1  2  5  1  2  5  1  2  5  1  2  3  1  2  3
1  2  3  4  2  3  4  2  3  4  2  3  4  2  3  4  2  3
1  2  3  1  6  3  1  2  5  1  2  3  1  2  3  4  2  3
4  2  3  1  2  5  1  2  5  1  2  5  1  2  3  4  2  3
4  2  3  4  2  3  1  6  3  1.
```

Make up a *frequency distribution table*.

SCORE	TALLY	FREQUENCY	TOTAL
1	⌋⌡⌠ ⌋⌡⌠ ⌋⌡⌠ ⌋⌡⌠ ‖‖‖	24	⎫
2	⌋⌡⌠ ⌋⌡⌠ ⌋⌡⌠ ⌋⌡⌠ ⌋⌡⌠ ⌋⌡⌠ ‖	31	⎬ 78
3	⌋⌡⌠ ⌋⌡⌠ ⌋⌡⌠ ⌋⌡⌠ ‖‖‖	23	⎭
4	⌋⌡⌠ ⌋⌡⌠	10	⎫
5	⌋⌡⌠ ⌋⌡⌠	10	⎬ 22
6	‖	2	⎭
		100	

From these figures the frequency of $(1 + 2 + 3)$ is three and a half times that of $(4 + 5 + 6)$.

By combining the results of a class, you should find (1, 2 and 3) turn up three times as often as (4, 5 and 6) i.e. ratio is $3:1$.

The larger the sample space, the closer to $3:1$ your results will be.

The hexahexaflexagon can be made very attractive by colouring (colours corresponding with the numbers) or by using the imagination to create patterns or pictures. Here are some suggestions.

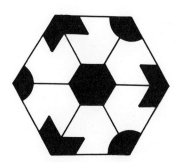

The cube

Nature provides us with examples of cubes in the shape of salt crystals (NaCl). We can fill space with them.

A cube can be painted in thirty different ways if the faces are each painted in a different colour, i.e. if six colours are used.

Mental images

Visualise these questions and answer them without sketching diagrams or using blocks.

How many faces would be visible if the following congruent cubes were placed on a level table?

	Exposed faces
* • 2 cubes, side by side	8
• 3 cubes, side by side in a row	....
• 3 cubes in a column (vertically)	....
• 4 cubes in a horizontal square	....
• 4 cubes in a vertical square	....
• 2 separate rows of 3 cubes each	....
• 8 cubes in a horizontal square (hole in middle)	....
• 9 cubes in a solid horizontal square	....
• 8 cubes arranged into a solid cube	....
• 12 cubes in groups as follows:	
1 alone, 6 in a column and 5 in a row	....
• A rectangular prism of 12 cubes arranged $3 \times 2 \times 2$	....
• The T-pentomino, flat on the table	....

Cubic capers

If a cube is sliced in various ways, the cross-sections or cut surfaces form interesting geometrical shapes.

When cut horizontally or vertically, the cross-section is a square which has an area equal to s^2.

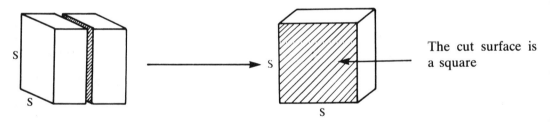

The cut surface is a square

VERTICAL CUT

The cut divides the cube into two congruent square (or rectangular) prisms, equal in volume.

Two triangular prisms are formed if the cube is sliced diagonally.

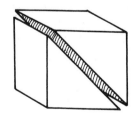

What is the cut surface this time?
Could you sketch the net of one of the prisms?

76

If the cube has a side of 6 cm, determine the length of all edges of the net.

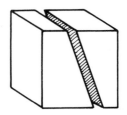

What is the cut surface if the cube is cut obliquely?
(See diagram.)

Would it be possible to make a triangular cross-section?

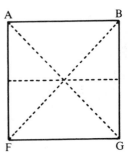

When cut in the following way, a hexagonal cross-section is formed!
How many surfaces has each part?
(See construction later.)

2 cm

* Problem corner
If the side of the cube is 2 cm and the midpoints are joined, calculate the length of AB (a surd!).
   Assuming it is a regular hexagon, calculate the area, in square centimetres.

An intriguing cube

Step 1   Take a square of paper, side 24 cm, and fold in the two diagonals and the horizontal axis of symmetry.

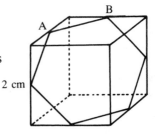

Step 2   Fold as in Diagram 2. Crease firmly.

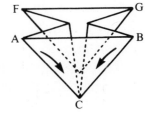

Step 3   Fold points A and B downwards to C.
Turn over and repeat for points F and G.
You now have a smaller square, ODCE.
Crease carefully.

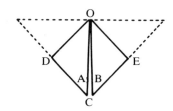

Step 4   Fold the front vertices D and E inwards, to touch
the diagonal OC.
Turn the square over and repeat for the other two
vertices on the back.

Step 5   Fold points H and K outwards.
Repeat procedure on back.

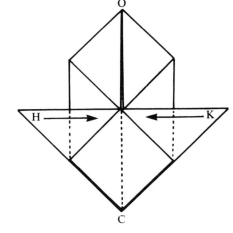

Step 6   Fold points H and K inwards to the centre.
Repeat on the back.

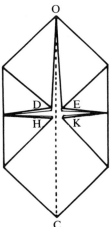

Step 7   Pull out the larger triangular section (with vertex
D) then tuck smaller front triangular section (with
vertex H) into the slit in section D. Repeat for K
into E and on the back.

78

Step 8   Blow into the small hole at vertex O to inflate the
            cube. Crease edges.

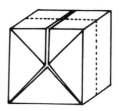

The puzzle cube – a dissection

A construction in three pieces.

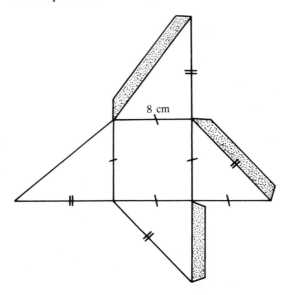

8 cm

Cut three of these nets from thin cardboard and assemble each to make a square-based slanted pyramid. Equal sides have been marked.

The three pyramids will fit together to make a cube.

This model illustrates the fact that the volume of a pyramid is one third the area of the base multiplied by the height.

Construction

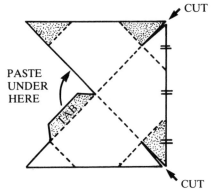 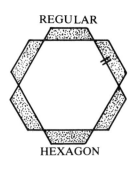

Cut two of each of the shapes shown. The sides of the original square are trisected. Paste the small shaded triangles under their adjacent triangles. Fit the hexagon onto the back and glue securely.

When the two pieces are complete, place the hexagons together to make a cube.

A flexi-cube

An 'open' cube may be flexed inside out, without tearing, by folding it only along its face diagonals.

- Cut a rectangle 33 cm long out of stiff paper. Mark off the lines as shown. Crease all the diagonals. Paste tab to other end to form an 'open' cube.
  Mark the inside by dotting or colouring.

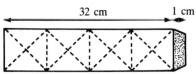

- Label the vertices, both inside and outside, as shown.

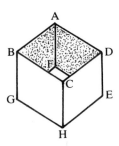

Step 1   Push corner C into the cylinder, down to F, pulling corners B and D together.

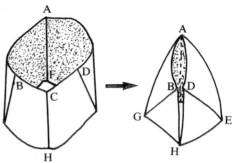

Step 2   Corner C is now pulled through until E and G come together.

         Flatten.

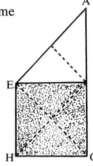

Step 3   Corners E and G are now pulled apart and A is pulled into the 'pocket' to meet C, to form a triangular model.

Step 4   Unfold model. It is inside out!

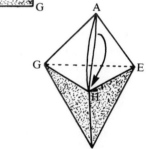

More activities with patterns

Straw experiments

Much enjoyment can be gained by learning geometry by practical means. One favourite set of experiments involves the use of drinking straws, threaded with wool or string or attached at the vertices with pipe cleaners.

Start by making the family of quadrilaterals. It will soon be obvious that quadrilaterals are most unstable as all the models can be sheared to one side, e.g., a rectangle shears to become a parallelogram, a square to a rhombus etc.

What would keep the quadrilaterals rigid? Obviously one diagonal, dividing the shapes into two triangles is all that is needed. This makes the quadrilateral rigid and its shape is retained no matter which way it is placed.

Write, draw or photograph illustrations of places where triangles are used in everyday construction.

Now investigate the rigidity of solids. Cut the straws to suitable lengths and thread with wool to make a cube and a rectangular prism. The 'skeletons' will collapse. Insert a number of face diagonals until the model becomes stable.

Can it be done? Try one body diagonal. Is that sufficient?

What is the minimum number of diagonals needed?

Some types of polyhedra do not change because they already have triangular faces. Can you name and sketch some common ones? Test by constructing straw skeletons.

The geometry of soap bubbles

A man is a bubble descending from God and the dew of heaven, from a tear and a drop of rain.

(Greek proverb)

People have been captivated by the exquisite geometrical perfection and muted colours of soap bubbles for centuries. Their charm is unquestionable.

The first person to have studied the geometry of soap bubbles and soap films, systematically, appears to have been the Belgian physicist Joseph A. Plateau. He did his research over a century ago.

In physics, there are many laws about forces in nature which are well known. Newton's law of gravity is one. Many of them illustrate problems of *maxima* and *minima*.

Experiments

Make a mixture of roughly equal amounts of water and commercial dishwashing detergent. A small amount of glycerin could also be added to stabilize the films and bubbles.

Take a thistle funnel and dip it in the soap solution. Blow air gently into the funnel. You will soon blow a hemisphere. Can you blow a bubble?

Now take a funnel or glass tube and blow some soap bubbles. Watch them land. If you can make them land on a deep pile carpet, by very *gently* blowing, the bubbles will 'run' across the carpet!

Bubbles always assume the shape with the *least possible area*. They illustrate that the sphere is Nature's choice to contain the most air for the least amount of area.

This is true whether the bubbles are in the air or in a liquid. Even a rectangular paper bag tries to take a spherical shape as it is blown up!

The surface tension of the liquid film tends to diminish the surface area of that film. Inside the bubble is a small amount of air, the volume of which determines the size of the bubble.

When two soap bubbles meet, what happens?

Each bubble retains its own shape until the instant the bubbles touch. The films flowing together eliminate part of the surface area of each, thus decreasing the total surface area and therefore the surface energy.

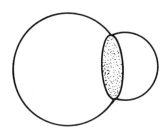

Plateau's three principles state:

1. A compound soap bubble, or soap film, spanning a wire frame consists of flat or smoothly-curved surfaces, smoothly joined together.
2. Surfaces meet in only two ways: exactly three surfaces meeting along a smooth curve or six surfaces meeting at a vertex.
3. When surfaces meet along curves, or when curves and surfaces meet at points, they do so at equal angles, e.g. when three surfaces meet along a curve, they are at angles of 120° to each other; when six meet, the angles are close to 109°.

To further these experiments and to investigate the geometry of soap bubbles, construct a set of copper wire 'skeletons' that may be dipped into a deep container. Students can easily construct a variety of simple shapes – closed and open – to start, then progress to such solids as the cube, rectangular prism, tetrahedron and, ultimately the dodecahedron. Thin wire can be simply twisted while thick wire will have to be soldered.

Suggested shapes could include:

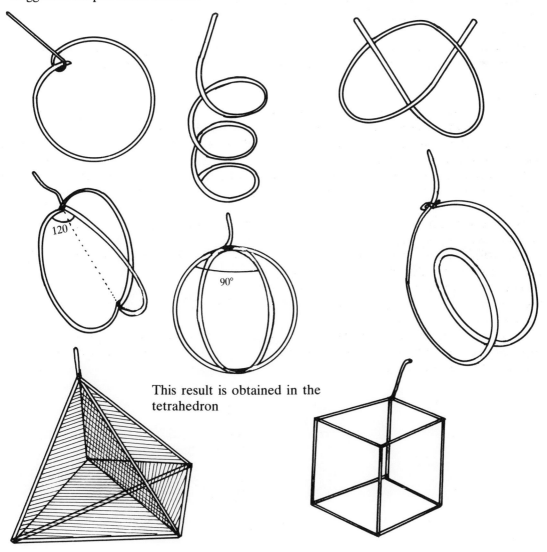

This result is obtained in the tetrahedron

83

These give surprising results!

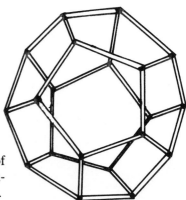

The study of such geometric properties and shapes, the area of surfaces and volume of solids has an application in the planning of roads between given towns as well as in other fields.

The dodecahedron

In the tetrahedron and cube, it is possible to calculate, by numerical means, the area of specific regions, the perimeter of given shapes and so on.

Note: In order to colour the faces of a cardboard dodecahedron such that all faces lying in parallel planes are the same, only four colours are needed; in the icosahedron, only three are required.

The explosive dodecahedron

Cut out the net of a dodecahedron from cardboard. No tabs are necessary. Divide it into its two congruent halves.

Now place the two half nets on top of each other like this:

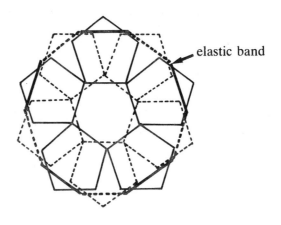

elastic band

Weave an elastic band around the model, alternating over and under, but keeping the cardboard as flat as possible. (It may be necessary to knot two long elastic bands together.)

Toss the model into the air and watch it 'pop' into a dodecahedron!

Topology teasers

You are all familiar with the Möbius strip and its many variations. It was named after Augustus Ferdinand Möbius, a German mathematician, who lived from 1790 to 1868.

The Möbius strip (or band) has been exploited by magicians for many years. The earliest reference to it was in a publication produced in Paris in 1881.

Occasionally the term *Afghan Band* has been applied to paper versions. Professor Hoffman illustrated the magic of this band as early as 1904.

Here is a baffling trick based on the simple Möbius strip.

- Place 2 identical strips of paper together (one on top of the other).

- Give them both a half twist and glue (or tape) the ends together – the two uppermost ones together and the two lower ones together.
- Run a pencil carefully around the shape, *between* the strips. Are they separate?
- Try to separate them. What happens?

Fit the result back into the double strip with which you began.

Felix Klein (1849 – 1925) was a German mathematician noted for his work in geometry and on the theory of functions. His programme (1872) for unifying the diverse forms of geometry through the study of equivalence in transformation groups was influential for over fifty years. He was a prolific writer and lecturer on the theory, history and teaching of mathematics.

In 1882 he invented the one-surfaced bottle that is named after him. It exists only in the imagination of topologists as it is impossible for the neck of a bottle to pass through itself, without the existence of a hole.

The impossible Klein bottle
A replica of a Klein bottle may be constructed easily from cardboard, using the following net plan. It is suggested that a small model be made first using 1 cm grid paper, then a large scale model be assembled using thin cardboard.

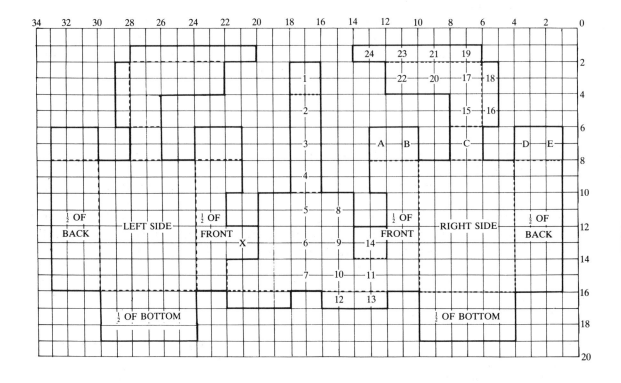

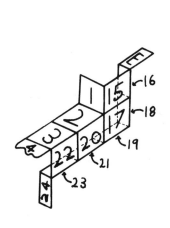

Units 15 – 24 make half the neck.

86

* Tantalising triangles

From thick cardboard (or thin sheet plastic), accurately cut out twenty right-angled triangles with the shorter sides 6 cm and 12 cm respectively. Arrange the twenty triangles into a square. If you find this difficult, calculate the area of the square, and therefore the length of one of its sides. Remember, the sides of the triangle are in the ratio 1 : 2!

Dice diversions

Any one of the five regular polyhedra can be used as a die (single dice). Known as 'dice of the gods', their regularity means that every face stands an equal chance with every other face of appearing uppermost when rolled.

Twenty-faced dice (based on the icosahedron) are made in Japan and are numbered 0 to 9, twice. They are used in sets of three to produce random numbers for sampling.

Dice similar to the ones we use today have been found in ancient Egyptian tombs and in the ruins of Babylon. Playing with dice was popular in Greece (the Greek for dice is *cubos*) and even more so in Rome. Dice were also used throughout the Middle Ages.

Investigations
1. How many different number combinations of four dice total 14?

   (e.g. ⚂ + ⚄ + ⚁ + ⚃ = 14)
      3   5   2   4

2. Study one die. You will notice that the sum of the numbers on opposite sides is always 7, i.e. 3 is on the side parallel to 4, 1 to 6 and 2 to 5.
Sketch the net of a cube and put the dots on it, in their correct positions and directions.
Use this fact to work out these three problems:

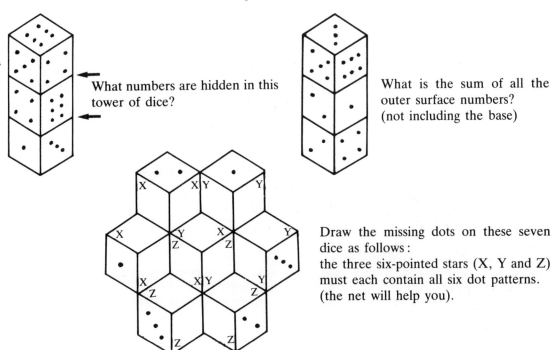

What numbers are hidden in this tower of dice?

What is the sum of all the outer surface numbers? (not including the base)

Draw the missing dots on these seven dice as follows:
the three six-pointed stars (X, Y and Z) must each contain all six dot patterns. (the net will help you).

87

Complete this table

Sum of 2 dice	2	3	4	5	6	7	8	9	10	11	12
Number of ways	1		3		6					2	1
Probability	$\frac{1}{36}$				$\frac{1}{6}$					$\frac{1}{18}$	
% probability (to nearest whole number)	3%				17%					6%	

Draw a line graph of the results (in the first two lines).

4. *Galloping dice*
- Ask a friend to roll two dice, while your back is turned.
- Ask her to add the two numbers on top.
- Ask her to pick up one die, turn it over so that the opposite face is on top, and add the new upper number to the previous sum, then roll the die again.
- Add the new upper number to the progressive sum.

You then turn around, pick up the dice and say your friend's total!

> *The secret:*
> When you turn around, find the total of the 2 dice on the table and add 7.

5. *Mind reading*
Ask a friend to roll 3 dice, while your back is turned. He must look at the uppermost number on the first die. Double it. Add 3. Multiply by 5. Add the number on top of the second die. Multiply by 10. Add the number on top of the third die. The sum is told to you. You can state the original numbers!

> *The secret:*
> Subtract 150 from your total and state the 3 numbers, in their original order!

Cubic illusions

Here are two tessellating patterns based on cubes. Trace them onto overhead transparencies then project them onto the screen (or wall) if you need to enlarge them. Trace again.

See how effectively they can be coloured by organising a class competition.

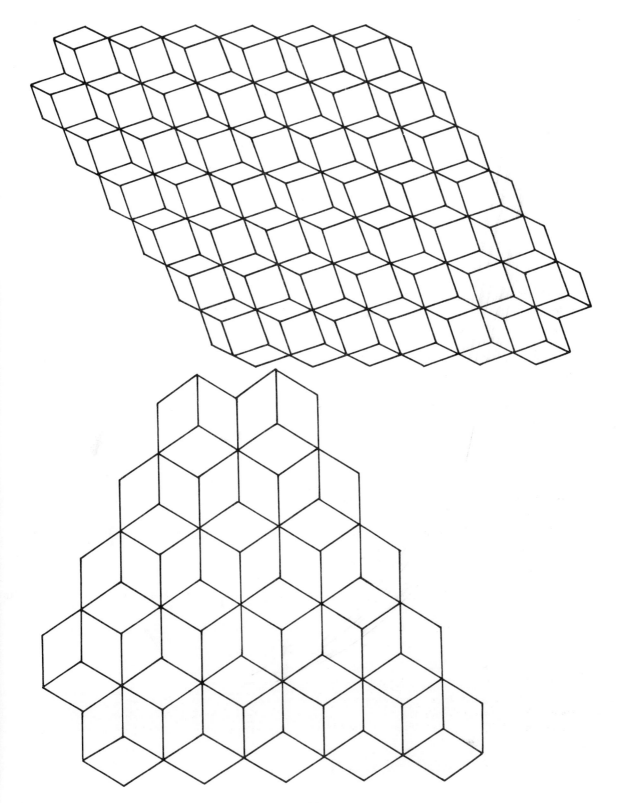

Graph gallery

Number 1 This lies within the first quadrant.
Before you plot the points you have to work them out correctly!

Point	x coordinate	Answer	y coordinate	Answer	Ordered pair
A	Sum of 2 and $1\frac{1}{2}$	$3\frac{1}{2}$	$4 + (9 \times 1)$	13	$(3\frac{1}{2}, 13)$ A
B	$21 \div 2$		0.13×100		(,) B
C	$3^2 + 5$		$y = 10 - 3 \therefore y = ?$		
D	Decrease 15 by $4\frac{1}{2}$		$17 \div 17$		
E	●●●◖ Fraction shaded?		$100 \text{ cm} = \ldots \text{ m}$		
F	$6 \times (3 - 3)$		1.5 m / 2 m Perimeter (in m)		
G	$(\sqrt{4})^2$		Average of 8 and 9		
H	$x + 8 = 18 \therefore x = ?$		$b \div 2 = 4.25 \therefore b = ?$		
I	Years in a decade		$7 - 1.5$		
J	$4.5 + 2.5$		If $a = 0.5$, $7a = ?$		
K	Number of sides in a quadrilateral		Change 5.5 to a fractional answer		
L	A heptagon has....sides		Days in half a fortnight		
M	$\sqrt{49}$		$8 + 3 - \frac{1}{2}$		

Plot the ordered pairs on a grid. Label all the points (from A to M). With a *pencil*, join the points with straight lines according to this order:

A	→	B	E	→	J
B	→	C		→	K
C	→	D		→	L
D	→	E	F	→	K
E	→	F		→	L
F	→	A		→	G
A	→	M	G	→	L
	→	L	H	→	L
	→	G	I	→	L
B	→	M	J	→	L
	→	L	K	→	L
	→	H	M	→	L
C	→	H			
	→	L			
	→	I			
D	→	I			
	→	L			
	→	J			

Colour effectively in 2 contrasting shades.

90

Number 2

A graph in the first and second quadrants, on 5 mm paper.

Point	x coordinate	Answer	y coordinate	Answer	Ordered pair
A	$\frac{1}{6}$ of 18	3	$48 \div 3$	16	(3, 16) A
B	$4^2 - 7$		$\sqrt{100} + \sqrt{36}$		(,) B
C	$3.5 + 2.5$		$10 + \frac{4}{4}$		(,) C
D	$\frac{1}{2}$ of 9		$\frac{x}{2} = 4 \therefore x = ?$		
E	$5x + 1 = 16 \therefore x = ?$		Prime number between 9 and 12		
F	$\frac{4}{5} \times \frac{5}{4}$		Product of 1, 2 and 7		
G	4.5×2		How many faces has a die?		
H	$1 + 1 \times 2$		Degrees in $\frac{1}{15}$ of a right-angle		
I	Whole counting number between -1 and 1		Even number between 4 and 8		
J	$\frac{4}{3}$ as a mixed number		$b + 11 = 19 \therefore b = ?$		
K	6×0		Prefix MONO means....		
L	$-4 \times \ldots = 12$		If $a = 2$, then $2a = ?$		
M	$-4 + 0$		-4×-2		
N	$+1 \div -1$		Halves in 4 wholes		
O	$12 - 21$		$\frac{6}{100}$ as a %		
P	$+6 \times -1$		Increase 10 by 10%		
Q	Half-way between -4 and -5		$14 - \frac{1}{3}$		
R	Increase -2 by -1		$2^2 + 3^2 - 2$		
S	$-6 - (+3)$		$8 \div \frac{1}{2}$		
T	$27 \div (-9)$		Minutes between 2.23 p.m. and 2.39 p.m.		
U	$12 - 12$		1.6×10		
V	If $2y = -2\frac{2}{3}$, $y = \ldots$		Average of 13 and 14		
W	$0 \div 3$		$\sqrt{441}$		
X	$2.5 + 2$		$20 - 6$		

Check your answers before plotting carefully *in pencil*. Label them A to X. Join, with straight lines, the following points :

A	→	B		I	→	E		O	→	Q
B	→	D		H	→	K		Q	→	N
D	→	F		K	→	M		P	→	S
C	→	G		M	→	J		S	→	U
G	→	I		L	→	O		U	→	R

T	→	W
W	→	X
X	→	V

Colour.

91

Number 3

This one, in four quadrants, is done on 1 cm paper.

Point	x coordinate	Answer	y coordinate	Answer	Ordered pair
A	$-3 - 3$	-6	$8 + 6 + 2^2 - (2 \times 7)$	4	$(-6, 4)$ A
B	Area of a rectangle 3 units by 2 units		$2.5 + 1.5$		
C	Halves in 3 wholes		$10 - 14$		
D	$(11 + 7) \div \frac{1}{3} - 60$		$-1 \times (+4)$		
E	25% of -24		$0.9 + 0.6$		
F	$2 \times -\frac{1}{4}$		$9 \div 6$		
G	Mean of 0, $\frac{1}{2}$ and 1		$\sqrt{2.25}$		
H	$(12a \div 6a) + 4$		Increase 1 by 50%		
I	$x + 5 = -1 \therefore x = ?$		$y + 1.5 = 0 \therefore y = ?$		
J	3 to the left of 1.5, on the number line		$-2\frac{1}{2} + 1$		
K	Product of -2, $\frac{1}{2}$ and $\frac{1}{2}$		If $a = 1$, $b = 1\frac{1}{2}$, then $3a - 3b = ?$		
L	$D = \dfrac{M}{V}$. Find D if M $= \sqrt{1}$, V $= \sqrt{4}$		$(-\frac{1}{2}) + (-\frac{1}{2}) + (-\frac{1}{2})$		
M	150% as a fraction		$-3 \div 2$		
N	25% of 24		Next number : 3, 1.5, 0,....		
O	To the only EVEN prime, $+5$, $\div 7$, then -1		The prefix TRI means....		
P	$\frac{8}{12}$ in its simplest form		Unity means....		
Q	$\dfrac{x}{7} = \dfrac{12}{28} \therefore x = ?$		0.99 to the nearest whole number		
R	$\frac{2}{3} + \frac{2}{3}$		$-1\frac{1}{4} + 1$		
S	What is the length of the side of a square if its area is 4 units^2?		$-1 - 1\frac{1}{2}$		
T	The origin has co-ordinates of (0, ...)		$-0.3 + -0.7$		
U	$\sqrt[3]{-8}$		$5 - 7\frac{1}{2}$		
V	$-1 -1 -1 -1 -1$		$0 \div 8$		
W	$2 - 5$		$25 \div 25$		

Number 4 A Galloping Horse
Take a piece of 2 mm grid paper and rule the axes, then number, according to these guide lines. Carefully plot the points, joining them with a feint *curved* line as you go.

(−5, 0)
(−4, 0.3)
(−3, 1)
(−2, 1.3)
(−1, 1.1)
(−0.5, 0.9)
(0, 1)
(1, 1.5)
(1.5, 1.8)
(2.3, 2.2)
STOP

(2.6, 2)
(2.4, 2.1)
(2.2, 2.5)
(2.6, 2.3)
(2.7, 2.1)
STOP

START AT
(2.6, 2.3)
(2.5, 2.6)
(2.8, 2.2)
(3, 2)
(3.2, 1.7)
(3.4, 1.2)
(3.7, 0.8)
(3.5, 0.5)
(3.2, 0.6)
(2.7, 1)
(2.3, 1.2)
(2.3, 1.6)
STOP

START AT
(2.3, 1.2)
(2, 1)
(1.8, 0)
(1.7, −0.5)
STOP

START AT
(1.5, −0.2)
(1.8, −1)
(2.3, −1.6)
(2.6, −2)
(3, −2.3)
(3.2, −2.6)
(3.5, −3)
(3.1, −2.9)
(3, −2.7)
(2.3, −1.9)
(2, −1.8)
(1.4, −1.1)
(1, −0.7)
(0, −0.9)
(−1.4, −0.5)
(−1.8, −0.3)
STOP

START AT
(−1.4, −0.5)
(−1.2, −1.6)
(−0.5, −2.3)
(0, −2.6)
(−0.5, −2.7)
(−0.5, −2.5)
(−0.9, −2.3)
(−1.2, −1.9)
(−1.8, −1.5)
(−2.2, −0.8)
STOP

START AT
(−2, 0.7)
(−1.7, 0)
(−1.8, −0.3)
(−2.2, −0.8)
(−3, −1.5)
(−2.9, −2)
(−2.5, −2.8)
(−2.3, −3)

(−2.7, −3)
(−2.8, −2.8)
(−3, −2.5)
(−3.3, −1.6)
(−3.5, −1.3)
(−3, −0.5)
(−3.3, 0)
(−3.4, 0.3)
(−3.2, 0.6)
(−3.7, 0)
(−4.3, −0.2)
(−5, −0.5)
(−5.3, −0.7)
(−5.2, −0.5)
(−5.5, −0.7)
JOIN TO 1st POINT

EYE CENTRE
(3, 1.6)

LEFT FORELEG
START AT
(1.8, 0)
(2.7, −0.5)
(3, −0.7)
(2.5, −1.5)
(2.4, −1.7)
STOP

(2, −1.8)
(1.5, −2.2)
(1.6, −1.8)
(1.9, −1.7)
STOP

(2.2, −1.5)
(2.6, −0.8)
(1.6, −0.5)
Put in nostrils and mane with a background if desired.

93

How well do you follow instructions?

(1) Print the word 'hypotenuse' in capital letters. ....

(2) Reverse the letters. ....

(3) Put the eighth and ninth letters, in order, at the beginning. ....

(4) Replace the first vowel with an A. ....

(5) Reverse the ninth and tenth letters. ....

(6) Translate the eighth and ninth letters into third and fourth place respectively. ....

(7) Move the last letter to seventh place from the left. ....

(8) Move the S to last position. ....

(9) Insert a G between the first pair of adjacent vowels. ....

(10) Substitute an R for the U. ....

(11) Delete (omit) the N. ....

(12) Replace the last vowel with an A. ....

What is the connection between the first and last words?

What am I?

Fit the letters in the lines below into the squares directly above to form words. Cross off the letters as they are used. The shaded squares indicate the end of a word.

B Y D E E N G S N R I I G H O U N I N D S
A . . T C A . O T . A S . B T . L D E E .

Word search

How many mathematical words can you find in this maze? You can start anywhere, then move one square at a time in any direction (horizontal, vertical or diagonal.)

It is possible to go back to a square already used but you are not allowed to double any letter unless you go on to another square. A score of 50 or over is excellent.

A	I	R	F	A	S	U	D	R	S	P	I
N	G	L	T	C	Q	L	A	P	A	O	P
V	E	I	T	O	R	U	B	R	N	I	E
E	S	N	D	D	U	M	E	I	T	R	L
N	U	A	E	Q	N	S	R	M	E	A	Y
I	P	L	U	A	E	O	A	R	I	R	E
M	A	N	D	R	T	B	C	E	T	U	A
E	I	L	F	E	S	U	C	A	N	R	N
L	A	M	E	C	S	I	V	S	L	S	P
L	A	M	I	T	D	D	I	P	L	M	O
E	I	N	O	A	E	R	N	A	O	I	S
M	T	R	E	R	C	T	E	D	C	T	E

Fractured words

There are over twenty mathematical words hidden in these three columns. Write a list of words, taking syllables from columns 1 and 2, 2 and 3 or 1, 2 and 3.

Column 1	Column 2	Column 3
bi	ne	ion
dia	tan	ula
tri	gram	or
inter	num	ation
co	sect	eral
pro	bola	ly
histo	nal	gent
right	llel	ber
para	form	ing
trans	angle	
sub	meter	
peri	val	
	est	
	gonal	
	tract	
	pose	
	efficient	

Magiwords

By adding the letter in column 1 to the right synonym in column 2, you find a word which is a synonym for the word in column 3!

Example : L + writing fluid   LINK = Join

1   D + frozen water......... =   spotted cubes
2   Y + organ of hearing ... =   period of time
3   C + unit.................... =   a solid
4   G + to free .... =   cross reference
5   T + capable .... =   set of multiples
6   F + highest cards .... =   surfaces
7   M + lyric poem .... =   score with highest frequency
8   P + narrow street........ =   surface
9   F + performer............ =   element
10 P + mixture of gases.... =   two of a kind

Decoding

Can you crack these simple codes?

* (a)   NZ EFGJOJUJPO PG B DJSDMF JT B SPVOE TUSBJHIU MJOF XJUI B IPMF JO UIF NJEEMF, KPJOE VQ TP ZPV DBO'U TFF XIFSF JU CFHJO.

* (b)   Z FNNFNK HR NMD ENKKNVDC AX NMD GTMCQDC MNTFGSR. VQHSD HR HM XNTQ ANNJ.

* (c)   Write a sentence of your own, combining the above two methods.

* Lines by a mystery poet

Each letter of the poem is represented by a numeral. When you have evaluated them, replace the numerals to decode the poem. Find R first.

Clues

$Y = H + 2M$ • $R = \sqrt{121}$ $E = B - A$ $O = A + L$

$R = B - H$ $A + 1 = S + V$ $S - R = T$ $G = S - 2M$

$I = \dfrac{A + D}{2}$ $S - 2M = 7$ $A = R + 4$ $R = A - C$

$W = 2L + H$ $M = \sqrt{N}$ $W = 2P$ $U^T - H = S$

$T^M = E$ $L = A + C - 5$ $D = A + C$ $V = S + H - N$

$F = 2B$ $2C = B - A$ $H = A - M$ $N = (A + H) \div 3$

15 4 14 8 16 8 11   18 29 5 9 7   13 2 5 19 8 9 2   9 15 3 8 19 2 29 3,

– – – – – – –   – – – – –   – – – – – – –   – – – – – – – –,

3 15 19 8   15   3 17 9 17 15 2 5 11 8   9 5 4 14 8 15 11   23 29 3 23,

– – – –   –   – – – – – – – – –   – – – – – – –   – – – –,

40 12 8 9   12 8   20 5 14 14 8 19   29 5 2   2 12 8   20 17 9,

– – – –   – –   – – – – – –   – – –   – – –   – – –,

2 12 8 11 8   4 15 3 8   15   7 11 8 15 2   19 17 9,

– – – – –   – – – –   – –   – – – – –   – – –,

15 9 19   13 2   20 8 2 8 11   13 15 17 19 ,   40 12 8 11 8

– – –   – –   – – – – –   – – – – –,   – – – – –

15 11 8   18 29 5   6 11 29 3?

– – –   – – –   – – – – –?

* Crossnumber with a difference

Across

1. Sum of the digits of 5 across
3. Sum of the digits of 6 down
5. One third of 9 down
8. Sum of the digits of 9 down
10. Sum of the digits of 18 down
11. 12 across minus 20 across
12. 10 down minus 7 down
13. 1 across plus 3 down
15. 16 down reversed
17. 13 down squared
19. 3 across plus 11 across
20. 13 down minus 1 across

Down

2. 1 across plus 10 across
3. Half of 2 down
4. 13 down plus 16 down
6. 15 across plus 7 down
7. 13 across plus 13 down
9. 10 down plus 17 across
10. 1 across squared
13. 15 across minus 8 across
14. 17 down minus 3 down
16. 3 times 8 across
17. Last 2 digits of 9 down
18. 8 across plus 17 down

A further challenge

The small digits in the *top* half of a square indicates a *horizontal* sum is to found, while the digits in the *lower* half mean a *vertical* sum is to be calculated.
No zeros are allowed.
There is no repetition of digits in any answer.

Some digits have been put in to help you get started.

Crossnumber

Across

1. Each digit is one less than the one before it; only one of them is even; no digit is 8 or more
5. A prime number
6. A perfect square with the first two digits the same
8. Divisible by 3
12. A multiple of 13
13. A palindromic number

Down

1. A prime number
2. Digits of 4 down, rearranged to form an even number
3. Each digit is one larger than the previous one
4. Divisible by 7
7. Cube 27
9. A multiple of 1-down; last two digits being the same
10. Last digit is the sum of the others. They are in ascending order; their common multiple is 84
11. A multiple of 11

Crossword

Across

1. I have 4 sides and my opposite sides are parallel
7. Two of my 3 sides are equal
9. I divide things into 2 equal parts
11. Five of these make 50
12. Six in ancient Rome
13. Take 49 from a mile
14. The price at which a shopkeeper buys an article
16. I have the shape of a tin
19. I help to keep things straight
22. 1980 is one of these years
23. I am part of the circumference of a circle
25. How to evaluate $\dfrac{144}{9}$
26. One more and I'll reach a score
30. I'm in the Greek alphabet
31. I have 3 straight sides
32. Once each year.
34. Take 499 from AIDS
35. North America and me

36. I am a short exam
37. It's odd that I'm not
39. From a fixed point I radiate
41. I'm not the length of a rectangle
43. I'm just right for the golf course
44. {1, 2, 3} is an example of me
45. An abbreviation for me is often obtained at the beach
47. I'm not false
48. Make it longer

Down

1. I could be square, rectangular or triangular
2. I'm an oblique square
3. I am a path to be followed
4. 60 km/h is an example of me
5. You can measure lengths with me
6. 3 is me in $3\overline{)24}$
8. Plural of 3 down
10. Find the value of ....
11. The metric system uses me a lot
13. I mean a thousandth part of it in the metric system
14. All my points are in the same straight line
15. Multiply by 3
17. I like this Japanese coin
18. A printer's measure which sounds like a letter of our alphabet
20. I'm one after 5
21. The sum of successive terms of a sequence is me
24. I am in the middle of every circle
25. Make me smaller
27. 5 eighteens make me
28. Move to a new position without rotating or reflecting
29. List all the elements of....
30. I am a flat surface
33. I am towards one side
38. It takes 7 of these to make 63
40. I am the highest point of a cone
42. Trigonometry (abbr.)
46. I am a shortened number

Mass-match

Suppose you have an unlimited supply of 1g and 5g weights. In how many *different* ways can you make 7g?   4g?

The answers form an orderly pattern if you work out the following table correctly.

Sum in grams	1	2	3	4	5	6	7	8	9	10	11	12	13	14	15
No. of ways	1														

Sum in grams	5	10	15	20	25	30	35	40	45	50	55	60	65	70	75
No. of ways	2														

Now you have only 1g and 2g weights. Complete these two tables.

Sum in grams	1	2	3	4	5	6	7	8	9	10	11	12	13	14	15
No. of ways	1														

Sum in grams	5	10	15	20	25	30	35	40	45	50	55	60	65	70	75
No. of ways	3														

Finally use 1g, 2g and 5g weights to complete this table.

Sum in grams	1	2	3	4	5	6	7	8	9	10	11	12	13	14	15
No. of ways	1	2													

Doubles

By changing just one letter per line, transform
- APE to MAN in 6 steps.
- ONE to TWO in 8 steps.

* Combinations

A safe can be opened by the correct combination of 4 digits.
By studying these sets of numbers, can you deduce the correct
4-digit combination?

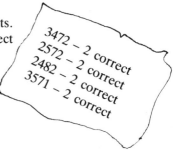

3472 – 2 correct
2572 – 2 correct
2482 – 2 correct
3571 – 2 correct

Area

Suppose three points on this dot lattice are joined with straight lines to form an enclosed shape.
What is the shape?

If four points are joined in a similar way, a square, with an area one square unit, results.

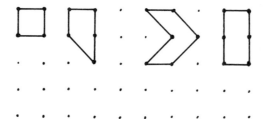

If five points are joined a trapezium is formed. What is its area?

On the diagram are two ways that six points may be joined. Do they have the same area?

Continue in this way, until you reach twelve points, then rule up a table and fill in your results:

Number of points used	3	4	5	6	7	8	9	10	11	12
Area of shape										

Write down a formula connecting the number of points (p) and the area (A).

Now investigate what happens if a certain number of points is enclosed within the shape (bounded in each case by four straight lines joining any four dots). The first three are shown.

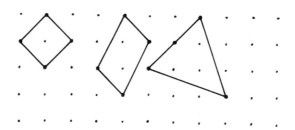

Make a table of your results.

Number of points on outside of shape	4	4	4	4	4	4
Number of points inside	1	2				
Area in units²	2					

Can you see any general pattern in the table?

Make a general statement that connects the number of inside points, the number of boundary points and the area.

Paradoxes

Here is a selection of paradoxes for discussion. Historically the earliest recorded one was: 'I am lying'.

1. An arrow cannot move where it isn't; it does not move where it is; therefore an arrow cannot move.

2. No horse has two tails. Every horse has one more tail than no horse; therefore every horse has three tails.

3. A bottle half empty equals a bottle half full. As doubles of equals are therefore equal, a bottle quite empty equals a bottle quite full.

4. $10 > 7$ is a true statement

   Subtract 14 from both sides
$$\therefore \ -4 > -7$$
   Square both sides
$$\therefore \ 16 > 49$$

5. If $a = b$,
$$a^2 = ab \qquad \text{Multiplying by } a$$
$$a^2 - b^2 = ab - b^2 \qquad \text{Subtracting } b^2$$
$$\therefore \ (a + b)(a - b) = b(a - b) \qquad \text{Factor}$$
$$\therefore \ a + b = b \qquad \text{Dividing by } (a - b)$$
$$\text{i.e. } a + a = a \qquad \text{Substituting } a = b$$
$$\therefore \ 2a = a \qquad \text{Dividing by } a$$
$$\therefore \ 2 = 1$$

6. Take a piece of 1 cm grid paper and cut out an 8 cm × 8 cm square. What is its area? Now divide it into the 4 parts as shown in the diagram, then rearrange them into the rectangle.

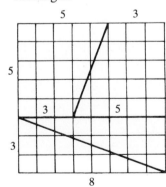

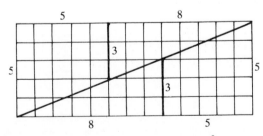

The rectangle's area is now 13×5 or 65 units².

Geometrical dissection

One of the oldest branches of recreational mathematics, dissection, is reputed to have been discovered by the Greeks, although the first systematic account seems to have been a book by Abul Wefa, a tenth-century Persian astronomer.

Pythagoras' theorem was probably shown by the dissection method!

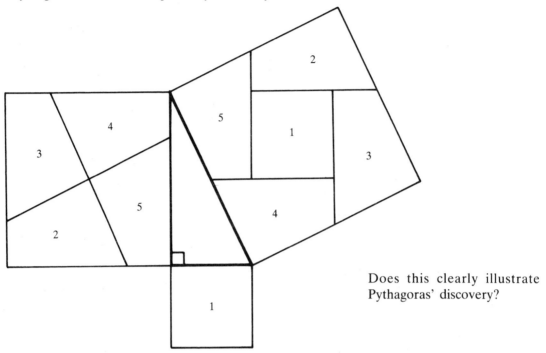

Does this clearly illustrate Pythagoras' discovery?

Transformation of squares to rectangular hexagons or heptagons was known at the beginning of the nineteenth century whereas rectangle-to-square dissections were described by the French mathematician Jean Étienne Montucla (1725 – 1799).

Tangrams (known in China as ch'i ch'iao t'u)
The famous dissection of the square tile into seven geometrical shapes has only been known since 1803. Many different theories have been raised about the origin of the puzzle and the coining of the word *tangram*.

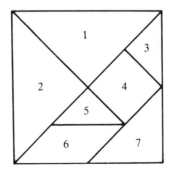

There are hundreds of interesting silhouettes that can be arranged with the tans. Here are some :

Cut a set of tangrams out of cardboard then try these activities :
- Make a square with pieces **3** and **5**. Which piece has the same area? Has triangle **7** the same area? Why?
- What fraction of **6** is **5**?
- Make a parallelogram with **1** and **2**.
- Make a square with the 5 small pieces equal in area to the square made with **1** and **2**.
- Make a rectangle with all seven pieces.
- Use all the pieces to form a triangle.
- By moving one of the larger triangles convert your triangle into a parallelogram.
- Calculate the lengths of the sides of all the pieces if the original small square (piece 1) has a side of *a* units.
- Work out the total area of the whole square.

These are some of the easier rectangle-to-square conversions.

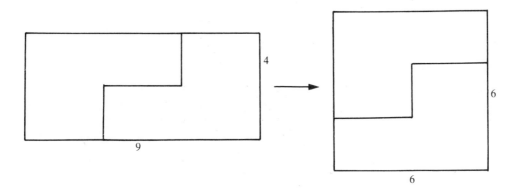

See if you can change a 25 × 16 rectangle into a 20 × 20 square. Use the step method.

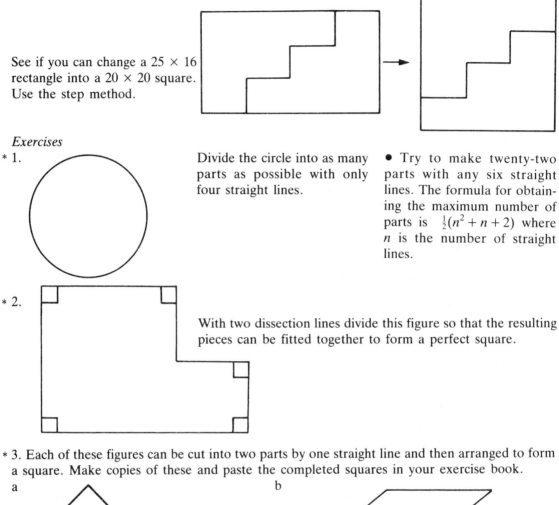

Exercises

* 1. Divide the circle into as many parts as possible with only four straight lines.

• Try to make twenty-two parts with any six straight lines. The formula for obtaining the maximum number of parts is $\frac{1}{2}(n^2 + n + 2)$ where n is the number of straight lines.

* 2. With two dissection lines divide this figure so that the resulting pieces can be fitted together to form a perfect square.

* 3. Each of these figures can be cut into two parts by one straight line and then arranged to form a square. Make copies of these and paste the completed squares in your exercise book.

a   b

c   d

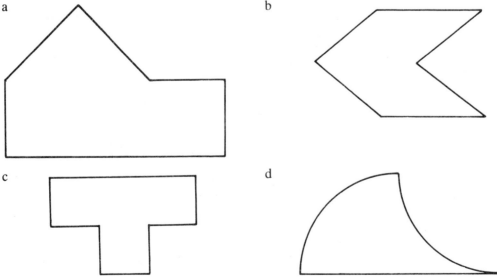

e   f

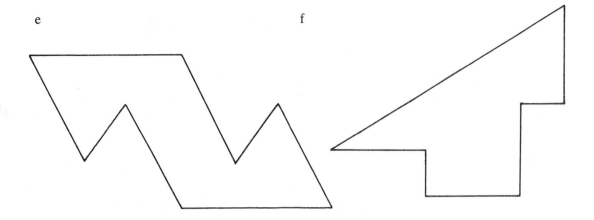

A 5 × 2 rectangle may be transformed into three or four pieces that form a square.

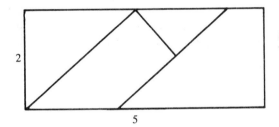

See if you can make the square.
What will be the lengths of its sides?

*

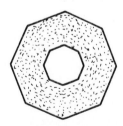

How would you cut this octagonal 'annulus' into eight congruent parts?
Rearrange them to form an eight-pointed star with an octagonal centre.

*This H can be cut into four congruent pieces, that tessellate (shown by broken lines).
Draw an accurate copy of the large H shape on grid paper then with one single cut, see if you can make five pieces that can be rearranged to form a square.
(Hint: make a symmetrical fold before cutting.)

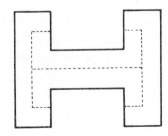

Sam Loyd's dissection of a square into five pieces, rearranged into other geometrical figures.

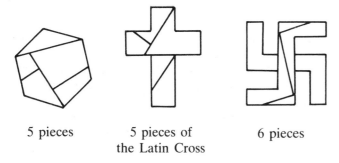

* *More difficult dissections*
Make a square from each of the following:

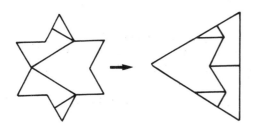

5 pieces   5 pieces of   6 pieces
               the Latin Cross

This six-pointed star can be changed into a triangle.

A tessellating dissection method, first discovered by the English puzzlist James Travers and published in 1933, is shown here.

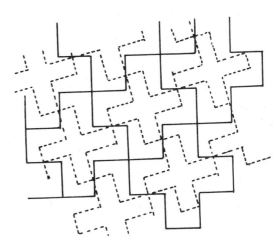

A tessellation formed by octagons and squares
The superimposed tessellation (dotted lines) is formed by a large square (with an area equal to that of the octagon), and a small square (congruent to the original small ones). It shows how an octagon can be dissected into 5 pieces.

Similarly, these tessellated Greek crosses are dissected into smaller similar ones.

Time

Your watch is a compass
If the sun is visible, hold your watch horizontally and point the hour hand in the direction of the sun. The direction indicated by a line midway between the hour hand and the 12 o'clock mark on the face of the watch will then be north if you are in the Northern Hemisphere, or south if you are in the Southern Hemisphere.

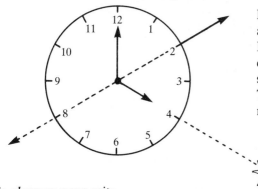

Directions calculated this way are only approximate.
It is necessary to divide the angle in half because the hour hand moves twice as fast as the sun.
The further you are from the Equator, the more accurate this method is.

To sharpen your wits
1. Calculate the number of seconds in one year. (Use a calculator.)
*2. If you counted once per second, how many years would it take to count 10^{10}?
3. Three bells toll at 2-second, 3-second and 5-second intervals. After how many minutes will they ring simultaneously?
*4. Half an hour ago it was twice as long after noon as it is from now until midnight. What time is it now?

* 5. The hands of a clock are together at noon and midnight. When are they together again? (as you are probably aware 3.15, 6.30 etc are wrong.)
  6. On 1 August, 1964 (1 – 8 – 64), the day, month and year were all in a geometric progression (i.e. the ratios 1 : 8 and 8 : 64 are equal). Counting the year 01 as 1, how many such dates have occurred or will occur this century?

Did you know?
February, 1976 had five Sundays. The last time that happened was in 1948 and it will not happen again until 2004! According to the two hundred and fifty year calendars, February has had five Sundays on only five occasions since 1784.

Seven

If you ask a person to state any number under 10, the chances are he or she will say 7. For many thousands of years it has been an important number in religious beliefs and superstitions, although it belongs to no special sequences, is prime and in fact, is not very interesting.

Such things as: seven days in a week, the seven deadly sins, the seven Wonders of the World, in seventh heaven, 'Seven Brides for Seven Brothers', '.... from seven circuits of the walls of Jericho....' (and more Biblical ones), all involve the number!

Do you know any more examples?

Even Shakespeare, in his play *As You Like It*, wrote this:

The Seven Ages of Man
All the world's a stage,
And all the men and women merely players;
They have their exits and their entrances;
And one man in his time plays many parts,
His act being seven ages. At first, the infant,
Mewling and puking in the nurse's arms.
And then the whining school-boy, with his satchel,
And shining morning face, creeping like snail
Unwillingly to school. And then the lover,
Sighing like furnace, with a woeful ballad
Made to his mistress' eyebrow. Then a soldier,
Full of strange oaths and bearded like the pard,
Jealous in honour, sudden and quick in quarrel,
Seeking the bubble reputation
Even in the cannon's mouth. And then the justice,
In fair round belly with good capon lined,
With eyes severe and beard of formal cut,
Full of wise saws and modern instances;
And so he plays his part. The sixth age shifts
Into lean and slipper'd pantaloon,
With spectacles on nose and pouch on side,
His youthful hose, well-saved, a world too wide
For his shrunk shank; and his big manly voice,
Turning again towards childish treble, pipes
And whistles in his sound. Last scene of all,
That ends this strange eventful history,
Is second childishness and mere oblivion,
Sans teeth, sans eyes, sans taste, sans everything.

In a lighter vein

- A seven-toed cat has given birth to four seven-toed kittens.
- Madeleine Tronson was the wife of the official executioner of France and the mother of seven sons, each of whom became an official executioner in a different French city!
- The most common kind of ladybird has seven spots.

Teasers

* 1. Take two apples from three apples and what have you got?
* 2. A farmer had twenty sheep. All but nine died. How many did he have left?
* 3. Arrange six coins in three rows of three coins.
* 4. How far is it possible for four sparrows to arrange themselves so that each one is the same distance from the other three?
* 5. How could you plant nine seeds in six rows with only three plants per row?
* 6. Six coins are arranged as in the diagram.

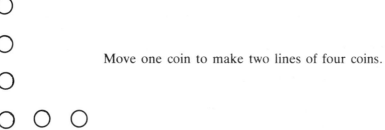

Move one coin to make two lines of four coins.

* 7. My mother has two children but her son is not my brother. Who is he?
* 8. Is it possible to put nine pigs in four pens so that there is an odd number of pigs in each pen?
* 9. What is the difference between the sum of all the odd numbers and the sum of all the even numbers, up to and including 100?
* 10. If a cork and bottle weigh 56g and the bottle weighs 50g more than the cork, how much does each item weigh?
  11. Write down any three digits. Reverse the number and subtract the smaller from the larger. Reverse the answer and then add the last two numbers together. What is your answer?
* 12.

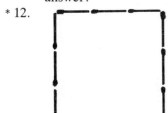

Without disturbing this square, add seven matches to divide it into three parts, of equal area.

* 13. Divide this square into four congruent shapes each containing the four symbols.

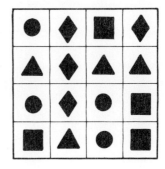

* 14. Seven coins are arranged in five rows with three coins in each row (see diagram).

Can you add two more coins to make it ten rows with three coins in each row?

* 15. Here are twelve counters arranged to make three rows of four counters and eight rows of three counters.
Rearrange them to make six rows, each of four counters.

* 16. What year is the same if it is read upside down?

* 17. In a container are sixty-six buttons, with twice as many whites as greens, one less blue than green and seven more reds than greens. How many are there of each colour?

* 18. Balancing.

* 19. Four candles, all different lengths, are lit at midnight. The shortest (an extremely slow burner) goes out at 5 a.m.
The others, although longer, burn five times as fast, going out at 2 a.m., 3 a.m. and 4 a.m. respectively. When the first is lit, the longest candle is 20 cm long. How long is the smallest candle?

* 20. Messrs. Carpenter, Baker and Mason live in Baker, Carpenter and Mason Streets where they practise the trades of mason, baker and carpenter. None of these men follows the trade, nor lives in the street his name suggests. Imagine how the postman mixes up the mail! Several times each week, Mr Carpenter re-addresses letters to his friend the baker. Who is who, and who lives where?

* 21. Three young working couples have the names John, Peter, Brian, Helen, Jane and Robyn.
John is a doctor. The occupations of the others, not in order, are artist, singer, pilot, secretary and novelist.
John is married to the artist; Helen is the pilot's wife; Robyn is married to the novelist and Brian is neither a novelist nor married to the secretary.
Who is married to whom?

110

* 22. In the shortest possible time write down the numbers in any three boxes that touch each other at some point (vertically, horizontally or diagonally) containing numbers that total fifty.

12	30	9	17	31	16
7	3	6	21	23	32
2	19	11	8	14	7
13	20	25	28	17	9
26	16	4	18	10	30
1	5	27	9	29	33

* 23. There are five daughters in a family, all with their birthdays on the same day and all under the age of twenty one. The girls were born at two-yearly intervals. If the eldest girl is exactly twice the age of the youngest and Denise was born before Debbie but after Diane, and Deidre is senior only to Donna, how old is Debbie?

* 24. What is the largest square that can be cut from a quadrant of a circle if the diameter is 8 cm?

* 25. What four-letter word ends in 'eny'?

* 26.
    3.19
    6.47
    8.25
    ―――
    8.73
    ―――

    This bill has the correct total, but the digits of the three items have been written down in the wrong order. For example 3.19 could be 1.39 or 3.91. Rearrange the items so their sum will be 8.73.

* 27.

Connect the matching pairs of letters, without the lines crossing.

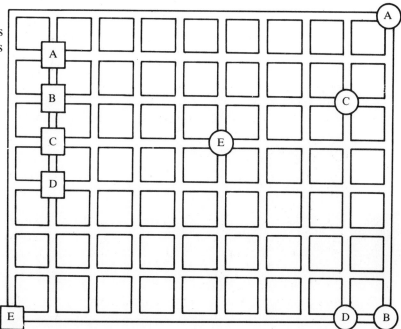

* 28. If a regular tetrahedron with each side of 2 cm is cut from each corner of a tetrahedron, side 4 cm, what is the name of the solid left. Sketch it.

* 29. Can you put + and − signs in the following so as to make 100?

    1 2 3 4 5 6 7 8 9

* 30. Insert + signs only to make a total of 1000 in 8 8 8 8 8 8 8 8.

* 31. In a village there is a barber who shaves all and only those men who do not shave themselves.
  Does the barber shave himself?

* 32. Arrange these numbers so that all the rows and columns total 33.

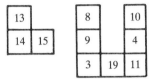

Hint : Try a symmetrical pattern.

* 33. A glob, under correct conditions of temperature, pressure and humidity, will double in size and then divide every minute. It takes one hour to make a bucketful of globs. After what length of time will the bucket be half full?

* 34. Nine balls look identical. They all weigh the same except for one, which is heavier. What is the minimum number of weighings needed to locate the heavy one?

* 35. In amongst a group of people there are some dogs. Twenty two heads and sixty eight legs are counted. How many people are there?

* 36. You have some pieces of dark glass. Each piece reduces the light passing through it by $\frac{1}{2}$.
  By how much is transmitted light reduced after passing through
  a) two pieces?
  b) five pieces?

* 37. Five children in a family are weighed and their weights recorded as follows :
  Elizabeth + David = 76 kg
  David + Ann = 84 kg
  Ann + Mark = 74 kg
  Mark + Carol = 50 kg
  Elizabeth + Ann + Carol = 100 kg
  What does each child weigh?

* 38. Without doing the multiplication, prove that
  $(1234567890)^2 - (1234567889 \times 1234567891) = 1$

* 39. A square garden has a tree 30 m, 40 m and 50 m from three successive corners. What is the area of the land?

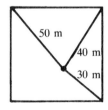

* 40. What are the necessary conditions that allow an isosceles triangle to be divided into two smaller isosceles triangles (using one straight line)?

112

* 41. Joseph, a Jewish historian, and forty other Jews were hidden in a cave surrounded by Roman soldiers. None of Joseph's companions was willing to fall into the hands of the Roman conquerors, so they resolved to kill each other. Joseph did not like the idea, but feigned agreement and proposed that all forty one men arrange themselves in a circle. Every third man was to be killed by the others till only one was left. Where did Joseph stand to save his own life?

* 42. To demonstrate your ability to add up an impressive column of numbers quickly, ask a friend to write down a line of five digits, then you write a line and you both repeat the process until it is a reasonably long column. Ask a friend to add it up, while you simply write down the answer!

$$
\begin{array}{r}
\text{e.g.} \quad 43072 \\
56927 \\
18944 \\
81055 \\
25087 \\
74912 \\
\hline
\\
\hline
\end{array}
$$

* 43. Is there a number that when divided by 3 gives a remainder of 1; when divided by 4 gives a remainder of 2; when divided by 5 gives a remainder of 3 and when divided by 6 gives a remainder of 4?

UNIT 5

SHAPES OF BEAUTY

Nature provides many examples of basic curves that we use in mathematics. The circle, spiral, ellipse, parabola and hyperbola are repeated often in plants, animals, minerals, liquids and gases. Of these forms, the circle is the most basic. Spirals are also common, being found in water currents, clouds and galaxies.

The three curves – the ellipse, parabola and hyperbola – that we call conic sections, have a long history. They were reputedly discovered by Menaechmus about 350 BC. They were further studied by the Greek geometers and then with renewed interest in the seventeenth century.

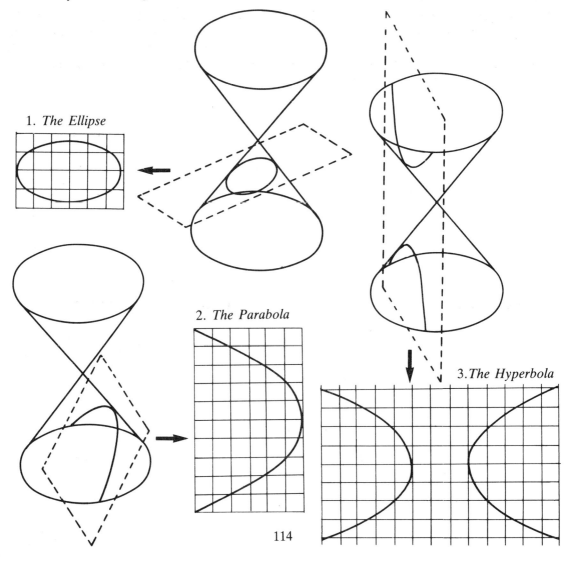

1. *The Ellipse*

2. *The Parabola*

3. *The Hyperbola*

The circle – a simple closed curve

All things from eternity are of like forms and come round in a circle.

Marcus Aurelius Antonius (AD 121 – 180)

One of the simplest, yet most useful curves is the circle, which to the Greeks was the perfect shape.

If a sphere is cut by a plane, what will be the shape of the cut surface? Can a cone be cut to produce a circular shape?

Our civilization depends on the work of round wheels, gears, dials, coins and plates. Motion in a circle is common, e.g. the tip of the minute hand of a watch or a horse on a merry-go-round trace out circular paths.

Can you think of more examples?

Basketball patterns

Suppose there are 12 girls standing in a circle. A ball is thrown around the circle, from one girl to the next one on her left and so on, until it returns to its starting point. In round 2, one girl is missed out; in round 3, two girls are missed out; continue increasing the number missed in each round. Draw diagrams to illustrate the patterns traced out by the ball. You should make some very interesting geometrical shapes.

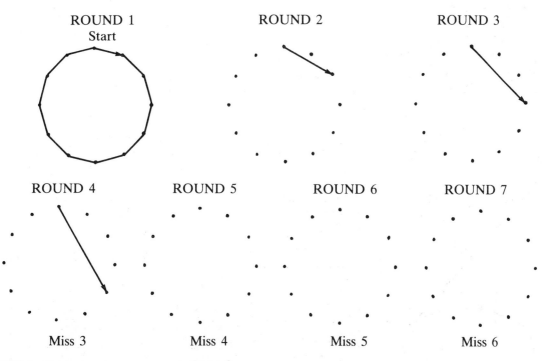

Which diagrams give congruent shapes?
Which ones allow every girl to participate?

115

The mystic rose

Divide the circumference of a circle, (radius 8 cm), into 24 equal arcs. The angle at the centre is 15°. Number the points 1 to 24.

With a fine pen, join each point to the 23 others. How many lines go to each point? How many straight lines are in the finished diagram? If your drawing is accurate, you should be able to see a series of concentric circles – formed by straight lines!

The ellipse

The planets of our solar system move around the sun (their focus) in elliptical paths. The moon moves around the earth in a similarly-shaped orbit, as do man-made satellites and space-craft. Johannes Kepler, the German astronomer (1571 – 1630), was the first person to discover (in about 1610) that the orbits of planets were almost ellipses and that the speed of a heavenly body in an elliptical orbit is *not constant*.

Scientifically, the path of an electron in an atom is elliptical. Periodic comets – those that return to our solar system at fixed intervals – describe gigantic elliptical orbits around the sun. Can you name one which is due to return in 1986?

Other comets swing around the sun in *parabolic* or *hyperbolic* paths then leave the solar system altogether, never to return.

What is an ellipse?

A simple illustration of the shape can be made by tilting a cylindrical glass, half full of water, to form an oblique view of a circle.

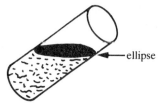

An ellipse has 2 axes – a major and minor one. It has the peculiar quality that if any point on the circumference is joined to the two foci, the sum of the two connecting lines is invariable (or constant) and always equal to the longitudinal axis.

This can be illustrated by the following construction.

THE TWO-PIN METHOD OF CONSTRUCTING AN ELLIPSE

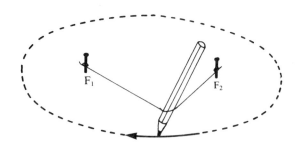

Securely fix two pins (tacks or nails) about 6 cm apart on a piece of card or on a board. These are the two foci, F_1 and F_2.

Attach a length of string to the foci. Keeping the string taut, use a sharp pencil (or piece of chalk) to draw an ellipse.

The ellipse made a comparatively late appearance in art since many primitive peoples did not have the specific knowledge of geometry needed to construct it.

In theory it is possible to work out a formula for the equation of an ellipse.

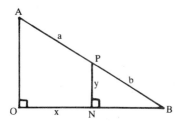

In $\triangle AOB$, since $PN\|AO$
$$\frac{BN}{x} = \frac{b}{a}$$

i.e. $BN = \dfrac{bx}{a}$

Now in the right-angled triangle PNB,
$b^2 = y^2 + BN^2$ (Pythagoras' theorem)

or $b^2 = y^2 + \dfrac{b^2 x^2}{a^2}$ (substitution from above)

Dividing both sides by b^2, providing $a^2 > b^2$:
$$1 = \frac{y^2}{b^2} + \frac{x^2}{a^2} \quad \text{or} \quad \frac{x^2}{a^2} + \frac{y^2}{b^2} = 1$$

This is the formula for an ellipse

Now let a = semi-major axis and b = semi-minor axis. If $a = b$, the equation becomes $x^2 + y^2 = a^2$ (multiplying both sides by a^2, then simplifying) which is the general equation of a circle, with radius a units.

THE SLIPPING LADDER PROBLEM

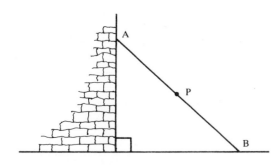

AB represents a ladder with a point P on it. If the ladder is held vertically up against the wall, then foot B is slowly pulled away along the ground while point A slides down the wall, what is the locus of P?

Draw a diagram in your book and accurately plot at least 6 positions of P. Remember that the ladder always remains the same length and P is fixed on the ladder.

This slipping ladder problem is employed to make an ellipse-drawing machine that is used in offices and by builders. The device is known as the *trammel of Archimedes*.

117

Elliptical endeavours

1. If two stones are thrown in a still pond, ripples will form sets of interesting concentric circles. Elliptical patterns can be found (see illustration).

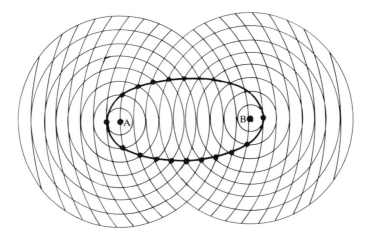

   Construct this pattern accurately in your book. Make A and B 8 cm apart and the circle with radii of 1 cm, 2 cm, 3 cm and so on.

2. Another simple method is to cut a large circle from a sheet of paper. Mark a point A, somewhere inside the circle (not the centre). Now fold the circle so that its circumference touches point A. Unfold, then fold again, using a different spot on the circumference each time. Repeat many times, in all directions.

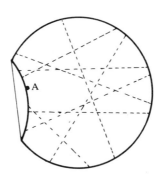

   The creases form a set of tangents that outline an ellipse, with A the focus.

3. In a similar method, a *mira mirror* can be used. Draw a large circle and mark a point F between the centre (C) and the circumference, Arrange the mira to map F onto the circumference (F'). Draw the mira line. Repeat many times.

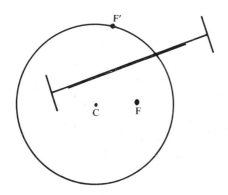

4. An ellipse may be constructed in a circle.
   Method I
   Draw rays from any point (F) in a circle. Erect a perpendicular to each ray at the point where it meets the circle. The envelope of these perpendiculars is an ellipse.

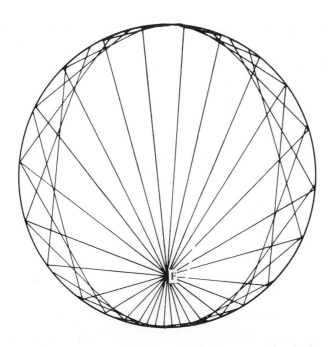

Method II

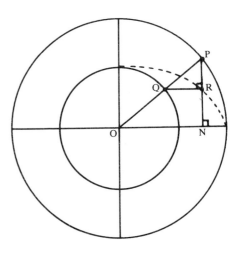

- Draw a pair of concentric circles centre O and radii *a* and *b*.
- Put in the 2 diameters, at right-angles to each other.
- Take any point P and drop a perpendicular PN.
- Join OP and let it cut the small circle at Q.
- Draw QR∥ON, to cut PN at R.

Then R is a point on the ellipse.

Repeat for many positions of P.

The outer circle is called the *auxiliary circle* of the ellipse.

5. In a rectangle

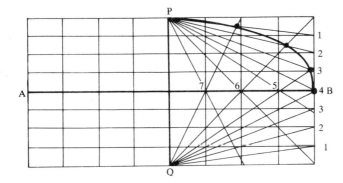

- Divide the major axis AB into an even number of equal parts.
- Divide the minor axis PQ into the same number of parts.
- Number the points as shown.
- From P draw lines to join and pass through points 1 to 7.
- Do the same from Q.
- Mark the intersection of P_1 and Q_7.
  Mark the intersection of P_2 and Q_6.
  Mark the intersection of P_3 and Q_5.
  and so on.
- Repeat on the left hand side.

6. Curve Stitching

Place a set square on a circle as shown, with the right-angle on the circumference. Draw in the chord BD. Repeat for numerous positions of the set square making sure that it touches F each time. This may be then be sewn with cotton if it is done on thin cardboard.

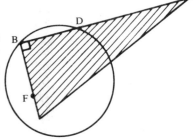

120

7. Reciprocal Function

On 1 cm grid paper draw a pair of parallel lines and number as in the diagram. Join a number on one side to its reciprocal on the other.

i.e. $\dfrac{2}{1} \longrightarrow \dfrac{1}{2}$

$\dfrac{3}{1} \longrightarrow \dfrac{1}{3}$

$\dfrac{3}{2} \longrightarrow \dfrac{2}{3}$

$\dfrac{4}{1} \longrightarrow \dfrac{1}{4}$

or generally $\dfrac{a}{b} \longrightarrow \dfrac{b}{a}$

Continue until a satisfactory elliptical outline is formed.

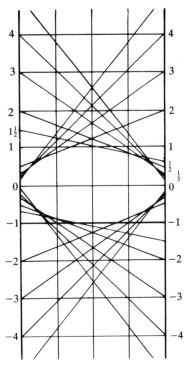

Elliptical gears

Cut 2 ellipses out of stiff cardboard (or plywood). Put a wide rubber band around the edge of each so that they do not slip. Place the 2 ellipses end to end and mount them on board with screws through the foci A and B (to act as pivots). Join the 2 remaining foci (X and Y) with a link equal to the distance from A to B when the ellipses are in contact.

Major axis $\approx$ 12 cm
Minor axis $\approx$ 9 cm

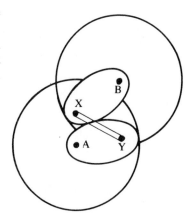

If one ellipse is rotated at a uniform rate about its fixed focus, the other will travel slowly, then suddenly speed up, appear to flick over sharply and then slow down again. This is the basis of a 'quick return' mechanism used in some machinery.

Elliptical facts

Often a loudspeaker in a radio, T.V. or record player is elliptical.

A ball lying on a table casts an elliptical shadow if it is illuminated from above. It touches the table at the focus of the ellipse.

The ellipsoid

A solid, with its axes perpendicular in three different planes and all of different lengths, is called an ellipsoid. The eggs of cormorants and pelicans are roughly ellipsoid.

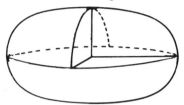

The cycloid

This is the path traced out by a point on the rim of a wheel (or circumference of a circle), rolling along a road in a straight line.

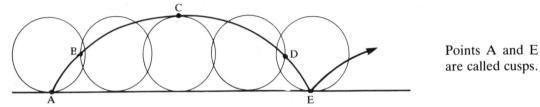

Points A and E are called cusps.

As the wheel rolls equal distances along the road, the point on the rim does *not* travel equal distances along its cycloidal path.

Distance BC > distance AB, for example.

What can you deduce about the speed of the point on the rim as it moves from A to B? B to C?

It is a fact that a given point on a tyre of a moving car is not moving at the instant when it is in contact with the road!

If the point moved 'within' the circumference of the same moving circle, or 'outside', the resulting rythmic curves would look like this:

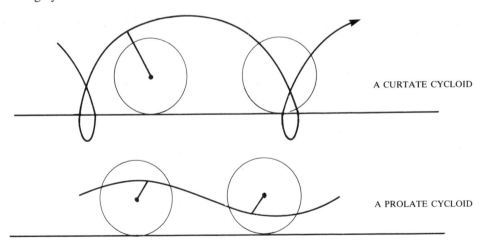

A CURTATE CYCLOID

A PROLATE CYCLOID

Rolling curves

Most solids which roll easily have a circular cross-section. Other shapes can roll as well. Consider elliptical rollers.

Make a model and carry out some simple experiments.

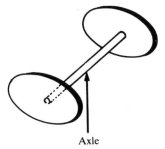

Axle

Trace the locus of the axle as the model travels over a flat surface.

Consider the shape formed by the intersection of 3 circles (A, B and C are their centres).

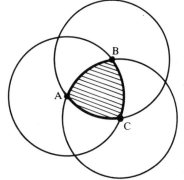

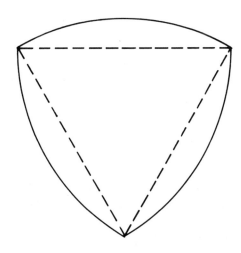

Make a template based on an equilateral triangle. Draw at least 5 positions of this unusual curve, as it 'rolls' along a straight line.

The parabola – the curve of falling objects

By definition, the parabola is the set of all points in a plane such that the distance of each point from a fixed point (the focus) is the same as its distance from a fixed line. Isaac Newton's statements about the universal laws of motion and gravitation were related to the parabola.

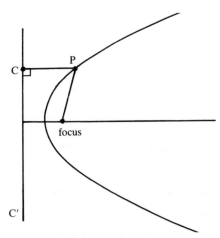

CC′ is called the directrix.

123

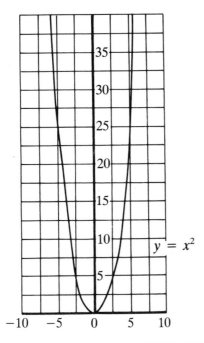

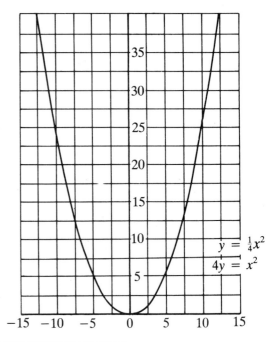

$$y = x^2$$

$$y = \tfrac{1}{4}x^2$$
$$4y = x^2$$

TWO PARABOLAE DRAWN TO THE SAME SCALE

There are many illustrations of parabolic curves: the stream of water from a hose directed upwards, the path of a basketball into the ring, the flight of a cricket ball and the fall of water over a precipice. In fact, every projectile, whether bullet, arrow, rocket or ball, will describe a parabola in its motion through the air.

Parabolae are used as the shapes for mirrors in the headlights of cars and for reflectors that bring radiation to a focus. Gigantic parabolae are used in the saucers of modern telescopes.

The parabola's most important property is that if a bulb is placed at its focus all the light striking the parabolic surface is reflected in parallel lines. Car headlights, searchlights and beamed radio transmissions use this principle.

The angle of incidence is equal to the angle of reflection (if there are tangents drawn to the curved surface at the point at which the light is reflected).

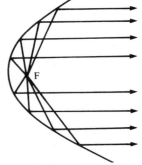

Similarly, a parabolic surface is used to collect heat from sunlight, with the sun's parallel rays being concentrated on the focus. In World War II the Germans tried to design a sun gun using this principle, but it proved impractical.

There is an ancient legend that Archimedes designed parabolic burning mirrors which set the Roman fleet alight during the siege of Syracuse, in which he later died!

124

The hyperbola

The boom from a supersonic jet is a shock 'cone' trailing the jet. The intersection of the cone with the ground is a hyperbola. At approximately the same time the boom is heard at all points on the hyperbola and within it.

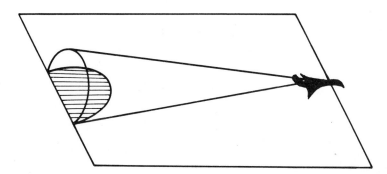

Remember though, that the hyperbola is normally a curve with two branches.

The relationship between foci and points on the hyperbola is used in navigation in a system called LORAN (LOng RAnge Navigation) based on the use of radar. Two broadcasting stations on land represent the foci. If they both send out a pulse signal, the navigator on the ship with LORAN equipment is able to calculate the difference in distance the pulses have travelled (at the speed of light), and so pinpoint the position of the ship.

The catenary

This is a curve formed by a string or chain suspended between two supports. It is not a conic section as it cannot be obtained by 'slicing' a cone. The formula for a catenary is
$y = \frac{1}{2}(e^x + e^{-x})$.

It also appears in three dimensions. If a soap bubble forms between two circular wire frames, the surface formed between the rings is that of the least surface area, with both outlines being catenaries.

The curve of music – the sine wave

Sounds, such as music on radio and television, travel through air. One mathematical expression for this wave motion is denoted by the sine curve ($y = \sin x$) where x is the measurement of the angle and y represents the distance travelled. It is called a periodic curve as it repeats itself after 360°.

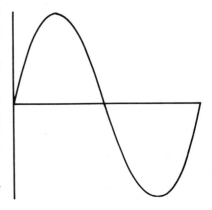

To illustrate the similarity between sound waves and the sine curve, attach a pencil to the end of a large tuning fork. Strike the fork to make it vibrate violently and pull it at a uniform rate over a piece of paper. The pencil will trace a periodic curve. The curve will have a greater height if the fork has a loud sound. A shorter fork of higher pitch will vibrate faster and result in a shorter wave length.

The music from a record player cannot be shown by a simple sine wave for it is a combination of tones and overtones of many instruments that are blended harmoniously.

Tuning fork : 256 cycles/sec

Viola : 290 cycles/sec

Human voice : 165 ± cycles/sec

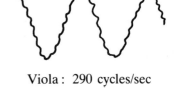

Whistle : 3000 cycles/sec

UNIT 6

PEOPLE WITH INSPIRATION
FAMOUS MATHEMATICIANS

Ahmes (c.3070 BC)

The Egyptian Ahmes wrote the earliest known work on mathematics. Written on papyrus round about 3070 BC, the scroll contains a detailed account of the Great Pyramid of Gizeh. In the account, Ahmes refers to a 'sacred ratio', i.e. the golden ratio! The scroll is now kept in the British Museum.

Apollonius of Perga (c.262 – c.190 BC)

A contemporary of Euclid, Apollonius made discoveries about so-called conic sections. He also contributed to knowledge about astronomy, to the military science of ballistics and finally to modern rocketry.

In a book entitled *Conics*, Apollonius investigated all the curves which were known – circles, ellipses, parabolae amd hyperbolae. He studied, and probably taught, at Alexandria along with his friend and rival, Archimedes.

Archimedes of Syracuse (287 – 212 BC)

Archimedes was one of the greatest physicists of all time. He was born in the Greek city of Syracuse on the island of Sicily. As a young man he travelled to Egypt, to study at Alexandria. Although his father was a distinguished astronomer, Archimedes concentrated on physics and mathematics.

On returning to Syracuse some years later, he devoted himself to science and became a prolific inventor of mechanical devices, perfecting such things as :

(a) A water-tight cylinder in the shape of a spiral, aptly called **Archimedes' Screw**. This was used to raise water for irrigation and for pumping out ships' holds.

(b) **Levers and pulleys**. He found proofs of the mathematical laws of the lever.
'Give me a lever long enough and a place to stand and I will move the earth', he said.

(c) **Catapults**, which he used to launch huge rocks at Roman ships laying siege to Syracuse. They kept the Roman army at bay for three years! Eventually the city was conquered.

(d) **Mirrors** to generate heat.

You can understand why he was called the Father of Engineering. One popular story tells how he ran naked through the Sicilian streets shouting 'Eureka! Eureka!' meaning 'I have found it!' He had realised, when sitting in his bath, that a solid placed in a liquid displaced its own weight of that liquid. This is one of the basic laws of hydrostatic engineering! Mathematically, he made many important discoveries.

(a) As most Greeks had no simple way of writing very large numbers, Archimedes devised his own system. He worked out a way of writing a large number such as 10^{63}, representing the number of grains of sand that could be contained in a sphere the size of the universe. His scientific book, called *The Sand Reckoner*, set forth a system of numbers based on the Greek myriad (or 10 000). Numbers up to a myriad of myriads (or 100 million) he called the 'First Order of Numbers'.

(b) Using polygons inscribed around a circle (up to a 96-sided polygon) he approximated π as being between $3\frac{10}{71}$ (3.1416) and $3\frac{1}{7}$ (3.14085) by using Eudoxus' systematic 'method of exhaustion'. He calculated the ratios of the polygons to the circumference of the circle.

(c) Using a similar method, Archimedes worked out a way of finding the area of a segment of a parabola – the forerunner of the ideas of modern *calculus*.

(d) He investigated the spiral, conforming to the formula $r = a\theta$.

(e) Analytically, he justified his findings about the centroid of a semi-circle.

(f) Using geometry as a tool for measurement, he calculated a formula for the surface of a sphere.

However, the discovery that pleased him most was how to calculate the volume of a sphere; that is, two-thirds of the volume of the smallest cylinder that will enclose it.

At his request, a diagram representing this information was engraved on his tombstone when he died in 212 BC at the hands of a Roman soldier. A battle was raging over Syracuse at the time. According to reports, the soldier became angry when Archimedes refused to stop working on geometric figures he had drawn in the sand of a courtyard. He protested that the soldier had interrupted his thoughts! The soldier killed him.

The loculus of Archimedes

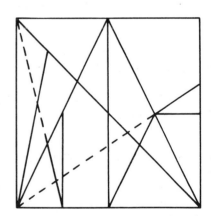

- Take a piece of coloured paper, about 10 cm square.
- Carefully divide it into 14 pieces as indicated on this diagram.
- Rearrange the pieces into an interesting silhouette.
- Paste the finished shape into your book.

Aristarchus of Samos (c.270 BC)

A contemporary of Eratosthenes and Archimedes, Aristarchus was in the forefront of a distinguished line of astronomers who contributed to 'Ptolemaic synthesis'. He made the first recorded estimates both of the diameters of the sun and moon and the distance of the latter from the earth.

The earth to him was a sphere that rotated on its axis and revolved around a stationary sun.

Aristotle (384 – 322 BC)

Born in Syria, Aristotle was regarded as the greatest of the Greek philosophers. He included some mathematics in his works, such as representing unknown quantities by symbols and suggesting a Theory of Combinations.

Bolyai (1802 – 1860)

At the age of 21, this Hungarian officer had established his hyperbolic geometry.

Girolamo Cardano (1501 – 1576)

An Italian physician, Cardano was also a great algebraist who investigated, amongst other things, negative and complex roots of equations . In 1545 he published a book on algebra. It contained Tartaglia's solution of the general cubic equation ($x^3 + Ax^2 + Bx + C = 0$), which Cardano had published without his permission. This caused a bitter debate.

Cardano was also famous for his scientific and philosophical writings.

René Descartes (1596 – 1650)

A a young boy, Descartes was very frail, spending much time studying in bed. In 1616, he graduated in law from the University of Poitiers. At this time, he was deeply dissatisfied with what he had learnt of the world's knowledge.

While camped beside the Danube River in November, 1619, Descartes dreamed how algebra could be applied to geometry. This opened up a new field of mathematics called Analytical Geometry, which nowadays is given the title CARTESIAN (or Coordinate) GEOMETRY, after him. He was reputed to be the first to use a, b, c to represent unknown numbers and to write x^2 instead of xx.

Later he settled in Holland and devoted himself to the study of science, theology and mathematics. Then in 1650 he became the teacher of young Queen Christina of Sweden, who insisted that she have her lessons at 5 a.m. each morning, in her unheated library. Descartes could not tolerate the loss of sleep and extreme cold of the Swedish winter, he soon fell ill and died of pneumonia.

Diophantus of Alexandria (c.250)

Little is known about the Greek Diophantus except that he lived in the third century BC and spent part of his life in Alexandria where he wrote books and treatises. One of these was called *The Arithmetica*, a Latin translation of which was printed in 1621. Diophantus did for arithmetic what Euclid had done earlier for geometry – he collected all the important unsolved problems in the theory of numbers and arranged them in a reasonable order.

He is known as the Father of Algebra, as he was perhaps the first to use a significant system of symbols in stating algebraic problems. One of his most famous problems is :

Diophantus' boyhood lasted $\frac{1}{6}$ of his life; his beard grew after $\frac{1}{12}$ more; after another $\frac{1}{7}$ he married; five years later his son was born; the son lived to $\frac{1}{2}$ his father's age and Diophantus died four years after his son.

At what age did Diophantus die?
If x represents the age he died, work out the following equation to determine this age.

$$\frac{x}{6} + \frac{x}{12} + \frac{x}{7} + 5 + \frac{x}{2} + 4 = x$$

We know by this riddle that Diophantus lived for 84 years.

He used ⋔ as a subtraction sign and devised other symbols to solve his Diophantine equations. The analysis of numbers that has grown from his work is called the Theory of Numbers and is the purest branch of modern mathematics.

A typical problem of the type studied by Diophantus was:

Find two integers such that when one forms their product and adds the square of either integer to it, the result will be a square.

Albert Einstein (1879 – 1955)

One of the greatest scientists of all time, Einstein was born in Ulm, Germany. As a boy he taught himself calculus and other topics in higher mathematics and science. Later he went to a Swiss college and in 1902 secured a position in the Swiss Patent Office in Berne, where he began writing extensively on physics and mathematics. In 1905 he introduced his famous formula $E = mc^2$ in his first published article on the theory of relativity. This theory led to the discovery of nuclear energy.

His dream was to find a mathematical formula that would unify all the forces of nature such as gravity, electricity and atomic energy. Einstein's brilliant discoveries were based on mathematical reasoning, not on experiments. He used ideas from non-Euclidean geometry in his thinking.

One of his greatest worries was that mankind would misuse the power which he had helped to release through the mastery of the forces of nature.

Eratosthenes of Alexandria (c.276 – 194 BC)

After Alexander the Great conquered Egypt in 332 BC, he ordered a city to be built and had it named Alexandria after himself. It became the chief seat of learning in the Mediterranean.

One of the many brilliant mathematicians who taught there was Eratosthenes. A friend of Archimedes, he was a prominent poet and geographer who was given the job as the fifth librarian.

About 240 BC he discovered that Syene (near present day Aswan) stands almost on the Tropic of Cancer. He was informed that at noon at the summer solstice, the sun shone directly into a deep well there, producing no shadow.

He decided to measure on the same day the shadow cast by a rod at Alexandria at noon. He found that the sun struck the earth at an angle of $7\frac{1}{5}°$ ($\frac{1}{50}$ of 360°) off the vertical. He knew that the sun's rays travelled in parallel straight lines, so concluded that the earth must be curved.

From this angle, he set about calculating the radius and therefore the circumference of the earth. As the angle was $\frac{1}{50}$ of a complete revolution he surmised that the distance between the two cities was $\frac{1}{50}$ of the circumference.

He is also known for his sieve method of obtaining primes. In theory, this system would give you all the primes if you kept going long enough, but as the numbers get larger, the task becomes extremely difficult. Because of this, the total number of primes cannot be obtained with the sieve. (Euclid proved that the number of primes is infinite.)

Euclid of Alexandria (c.300 BC)

A Greek by descent, Euclid (full name Eucleides) lived and taught in Alexandria. Although he was not a great innovator, Euclid was a superb organiser of the mathematical results achieved by such people as Thales, Eudoxus and other learned Greeks. He was the first Professor of Mathematics at the Museum (the university of the ancient world, founded by Ptolemy Soter).

About 300 BC he wrote his masterpiece – a treatise in thirteen books, written on papyrus. It was called *The Elements of Geometry*, and it gathered together all the important works and knowledge of his predecessors. His writings, clear and terse, described and proved a great deal about lines, points, circles and elementary solid shapes, using only compasses and straight edges as instruments.

The first six books of *The Elements* dealt with triangles, rectangles, circles, polygons, proportion and similarity. The next four treated the theory of numbers, the eleventh book was an introduction to solid geometry while the twelfth dealt with pyramids, cones and cylinders. The last book was about the five regular solids. Altogether, they contained four hundred and sixty five propositions. Euclid's treatise was published much later in Venice, in 1482.

Euclid deduced all his information from five postulates and five axioms.
The axioms stated:
1. Things equal to the same thing are equal.
2. If equals are added to equals, the sums are equal.
3. If equals are subtracted from equals, the remainders are equal.
4. Things which coincide with one another are equal to one another.
5. The whole is greater than the part.

The postulates stated:
1. A straight line can be drawn from any point to any other point.
2. A finite straight line can be drawn continuously in a straight line.
3. A circle can be described with any point as centre and with a radius equal to any finite straight line drawn from the centre.
4. All right-angles are equal to each other.
5. Given a straight line and any point not on this line, there is, through that point, one and only one line that is parallel to the given line.

To describe his work, Euclid used the term 'geometry', meaning 'earth measurement' (from the Greek words 'geo' meaning 'earth' and '-metry' meaning 'the process of measuring').

Abraham Lincoln, one of the greatest presidents of the United States regarded *The Elements* as a splendid sharpener of the mind because it improved his 'powers of logic and language'.

Karl Friedrich Gauss (1777 – 1855)

Gauss was born in Brunswick, Germany to poor parents. He was a gifted student, even from early childhood. In his third year of schooling (at the age of 10), he discovered a quick method of finding the sum of the digits from 1 – 100.

When he was fourteen, Ferdinand, the Duke of Brunswick, helped pay Gauss' way through preparatory school and university where he mastered Greek, Latin, French, Danish and English. In the mathematical field he read avidly in algebra, geometry, calculus and number theory.

Arithmetic was Gauss' favourite field of study all his life. By the time he was 18 he had discovered new laws concerning the theory of numbers. He was very excited when he realised that every positive integer is the sum of 3 triangular numbers (e.g. $17 = 1 + 6 + 10$). Geometrically he worked out how to construct a regular polygon with 17 sides!

Regarded as one of the three greatest mathematicians of history, as well as a renowned astronomer of his time, Gauss was the first director of the famous Observatory of Germany's Göttingen University. This was built during the Napoleonic Wars. (Bernhard Riemann, one of Gauss' gifted students, was a later director of the Observatory. He ventured into the realm of non-Euclidean geometry and the curvature of space.)

Gauss was a friendly and humble individual, who lived modestly all his life. Newton was his ideal.

Heron of Alexandria (c.AD 75)

Heron established a formula for the area of a triangle in terms of its sides, invented a steam engine, a rotary steam bellows, a theodolite and other surveying instruments. He is known to have observed and described a lunar eclipse in AD 62.

Hipparchus of Alexandria (c.180 – 125 BC)

Hipparchus, who lived half a century after Archimedes, condensed the essentials of Greek geometry for the use of the astronomer and the surveyor. He was the originator of trigonometry; he measured the angles at the centre of a circle subtended by numerous chords. By compiling his results, the first trigonometric tables were devised – a table of chords.

Sea trade fostered the study of navigation and astronomy. Hipparchus originated the use of latitude and longitude for fixing geographical positions on the earth's surface. Frequent military campaigns called for more surveying and map-making and the demand for weapons of war led to a closer study of mining problems and mechanics.

Hipparchus also cited the length of the tropical year as 365 days 5 hours 55 minutes 12 seconds.

Hypatia of Alexandria (c.AD 370 – 415)

Hypatia, daughter of Theon, was the first recorded woman mathematician. She was among the last of the Archimedean believers (following the tradition of creative enquiry) and pagan intellectuals. Supposedly very beautiful, Hypatia was an exceedingly learned woman who lectured at the University of Alexandria around AD 400. Her annotated version of Euclid was the foundation of subsequent editions!

It is believed she was murdered by a wild Christian mob.

About AD 390, Theon, Hypatia's father, edited Euclid's *Elements* and the great work of Ptolemy. He also wrote various scientific treatises, and set forth a method for finding square roots by the aid of sexagesimal fractions!

Gottfried Wilhelm Leibniz (1646 – 1716)

Leibniz was a genius who won recognition in many different fields – law, religion, history, literature, logic, metaphysics and speculative philosophy, as well as mathematics. He attended the University of Leipzig in Germany, and by the age of seventeen had a bachelor's degree.

Later he spent much time travelling in Europe as a diplomat.

His version of calculus was published in 1684, at about the same time as Newton's. He popularised the use of the integral symbol in calculus.

Leibniz was a devout man who wrote much about religion. Even his invention of binary numbers was related to his beliefs. He considered God to be represented by 1, and the void (or nothing) by 0. Just as God could create all things out of void, so could all numbers be represented in the binary system using just 1 and 0.

He invented a calculating machine that could do the four operations and even extract roots!

John Napier (1550 – 1617)

Napier, who was laird of Merchiston in Scotland, invented and compiled tables of logarithms. He also used the decimal point, and wrote a work on computing rods and one on algebra.

Besides being a mathematician of note, Napier was an astronomer, an engineer and a physicist.

Sir Isaac Newton (1642 – 1727)

Isaac Newton was born on Christmas Day, 1642, during the Civil War. The son of a Lincolnshire farmer, he was a small and feeble child and as a boy gave little sign of his genius. At school he was very inattentive and ranked among the lowest in the school! His chief interests seemed to be carpentry, mechanics, the writing of verse and drawing.

In 1661 he was sent to Trinity College, Cambridge where he studied for the B.A. degree. This he attained in 1664, with his M.A. following in 1668. It was in this period of his life that Newton's genius began to assert itself.

Skilled as a mechanic and carpenter, he made toys, models, kites and even invented a water-driven clock. However, alchemy, chemistry and theology were his main interests, while physics, mathematics and astronomy were just diversions.

During 1665 – 1666 an outbreak of the dreaded black plague forced Newton to live at home. This proved to be one of the most productive periods of discovery in all mathematical history. His most important contributions included:
- the binomial theorem
- his version of calculus, called 'fluxions'
- the law of universal gravitation
- the theory of the nature of light
- theories on gravity.

To quote him on gravity:

Any two particles in the universe attract one another with a force which is directly proportional to the product of their masses and inversely proportional to the square of the distance between them.

By means of this principle, Newton was able to explain Kepler's laws, the behaviour of tides, the flattening of the poles and the motion of planets, satellites and comets about the sun. Is it any wonder he has been called 'the Pioneer of Space Mathematics'?

Even though Newton was a prolific writer, he was very reluctant to have his discoveries published.

He was elected fellow of the Royal Society in 1672 and was chosen in 1689 to represent Cambridge University in parliament.

In 1699 he became Master of the Mint in London. While there he pursued his theological studies.

Queen Anne knighted Newton in 1705. The latter part of his life was mathematically unproductive. He died in 1727, at the age of eighty four, probably of a heart attack. He was buried in Westminster Abbey, where his tomb may still be seen.

Plato (429 – 348 BC)

'God ever geometrizes' said Plato. He insisted that geometric proofs should be demonstrated with no aids other than a straight edge and compass.

It is said that Plato visited Egypt, partly for purposes of trade but chiefly to acquire knowledge. He began to appreciate geometry through contact with the Pythagoreans on a visit to Italy, and later his interest increased during his extensive travelling through Sicily and Asia.

The Athenian statesman and philosopher Socrates was a teacher of Plato, insisting that he base his mathematics on sound logic. Socrates left no writings of his own, but we have the testimony of Plato, Euclid and others that they were greatly his debtors.

Plato lectured for some time in the gymnasium of the Academeia, where his influence helped Greek geometry develop as an abstract science. Over Plato's academy were the words:
Let no one ignorant of geometry enter here – the oldest recorded entrance requirement of a college!

Ptolemy = Claudius Ptolemaeus (c. AD 87 – 168)

Author of the *Almagest* (meaning 'great treatise'), Ptolemy based his writings on those of Hipparchus, bringing together important knowledge on astronomy and trigonometry.

He estimated the moon's distance from the earth as being approximately sixty-one times the earth's radius. Unlike his predecessors, Ptolemy believed the earth was the centre of the universe but tried to show how planets, sun and moon moved around the earth. His ideas were accepted for fourteen centuries.

Pythagoras (c. 582 – 501 BC)

Pythagoras was born on the mountainous island of Samos about 582 BC. His parents were Phoenician. Little is known of his early life, except that he became a student of Thales, and on his advice, travelled extensively to places such as Egypt, Babylon and India.

When he was about fifty, he moved to Crotona, part of a Greek colony in Southern Italy. Here he founded an unusual semi-religious school and brotherhood which attracted around three hundred well-to-do young men who were dedicated to the study of mathematics, music and gymnastics as well as to the practice of mystical doctrines. It is known that Pythagoras was an athlete and a swimming champion, gaining prizes for running, jumping and wrestling. It is probably due to the Pythagoreans that boxing has attained status as a sport.

His school, known as the Order of Pythagoreans, soon began to have an influence that extended throughout the Greek world. Its symbol was the pentagram, which meant 'good health'. Discipline was very strict. Some of their rules and taboos included their refusal to wear wool clothing, to eat beans or meat (cows, sheep or geese) or to drink wine, to touch a white rooster or to stir a fire with iron. They took special care to keep the marks of ashes off their pots. Periods of long silence had to be strictly observed.

Strong religious beliefs enveloped the Pythagoreans' thinking. Immortality, reincarnation and transmigration of souls from man to man and man to beast were just some of these beliefs.

Pythagoras became something of an idol to the group. Members were pledged to secrecy and were required to sign up for life. Penalty for disclosing important mathematical secrets to non-members was death.

In spite of their doctrines, the Pythagoreans are credited with having been the first to apply deductive reasoning exclusively and systematically to the solution of mathematical problems. They were the first to describe numbers as odd or even. In fact, they classified the entire universe into categories that included perfect and amicable groups, believing that numbers were the key to all things in nature. Even numbers were classified as feminine, while odd numbers were masculine (except for 1, which they regarded as the generator of all numbers). Their symbol for marriage was 5, the sum of 2 (female) and 3 (male). Three was also called the 'perfect number, expressive of the beginning, middle and end,' making it the symbol of the deity. The multiplication table as we know it today was also credited to the Pythagoreans. They believed the world was a stationary sphere (having observed the shadow of the earth cast on the moon), and that it was the centre of the universe.

Following Thales' work in plane and solid geometry, Pythagoras insisted that axioms should first be established and that everything following must be reached by strict deductive reasoning. Pythagoras' famous theorem clearly demonstrates this. Although the theorem had been discovered over a millenium (1000 years) earlier by the Babylonians, the Pythagorean school is credited with being the first to prove it. This same theorem brought with it a shattering discovery – if the shorter sides of a right-angled triangle were one unit long, the hypotenuse was greater than one but less than two (as we know it, $\sqrt{2}$). They had previously thought of all mathematics in terms of *whole* numbers and ratios of whole numbers. Thus they called their new number 'irrational' meaning 'not in any ratio'.

From their investigations with geometry, they soon realised that irrational numbers came up again and again with astounding frequency. The ratio of a circle's circumference to its diameter is itself the irrational number π, 3.14159 ..... It is believed that the first letter of the Greek word *periphereia* (meaning periphery) inspired the π symbol.

The Pythagoreans also considered the problems of regular tessellations.

Musically, the Pythagoreans showed the relationship between the length of a music string and the pitch of its note, ultimately producing the octave. As Pythagoras said:

The beautiful in sound must depend upon a succession of notes related to each other and a prime by the simplest ratios.

The Pythagoreans concluded that all relationships in the physical world (harmony, beauty and nature) could be expressed in terms of simple ratios. They realized that the notes produced by two strings of equal diameter and tension would vary according to the lengths of the strings. In particular, they noted that if one string were half as long as another, the tone would be the same but from the shorter string would come the higher sound. This relationship illustrates what we call an octave, that is, the ratio of string lengths is $1:2$.

Therefore, given any string length with its note, by halving the length the pitch is raised by an octave.

The next simplest ratio, $1:3$, is smaller than for the octave, so the pitch must be higher. It is called the fifth. The Pythagoreans developed their entire scale by advancing the pitch by fifths.

If only one string is used, different positions on the string produce different notes according to simple fractions expressible as ratios of whole numbers, e.g. $\frac{6}{15}$ of a C string gives B; $\frac{6}{5}$ of it gives A; $\frac{4}{3}$ of it gives G; $\frac{3}{2}$ gives F; $\frac{8}{5}$ gives E; $\frac{16}{9}$ gives D and exactly twice it gives C again, an octave lower.

The four notes C, F, G and low C were the basis of very ancient Greek music. They are said to form the range of the legendary lyre of Orpheus.

Many of the Greek mathematicians wrote treatises on music, with fragments by Ptolemy and Euclid surviving. The Pythagorean music theory was preserved through the writings of Boethius whose textbook was a source of study up to the seventeenth century, mainly because of its so-called mystical qualities and its mathematics. Pythagoras believed orbiting planets gave off a whole harmony, which he called *the music of the spheres*.

Niccolo Fontana Tartaglia (c.1500 – 1557)

Tartaglia, whose name means 'the stammerer' was born to poor parents in Brescia. He grew up to become one of the most skilled equation-solvers in Italy. Tartaglia devised general solutions for cubic equations. Previously, a Franciscan friar, Luca Paciola, had published a comprehensive compendium of algebra called the *Summa de Arithmetica* in 1494. It contained methods for solving linear and quadratic equations. Tartaglia later gave a public demonstration of his method of solving cubic equations.

His treatise on arithmetic is one of the chief authorities for our knowledge of Italian mathematics of his time. Italian mathematicians used the first letter of the word più (plus) to signify +. Our plus sign is a shorthand form of the Latin 'et' meaning 'and'.

Thales (c.625 – 545 BC)

The Greeks were the first to pursue mathematics as an art for its own sake. Among the outstanding academics of the time was Thales, who came from the prosperous and important city of Miletus (now part of Turkey). There he was a very successful olive oil merchant who travelled extensively, setting up presses as far away as Asia Minor. Because of his success in business, Thales 'retired' early in life and turned his attention to politics, astronomy, arithmetic and geometry.

He is credited with having predicted a solar eclipse in 585 BC, a feat requiring remarkable skill at computing.

Thales is known as one of the Seven Wise Men of Ancient Greece.

By using his shadow-reckoning method, he astounded the Egyptians by calculating the height of one of the pyramids using proportionate right-angled triangles. This method was later developed into the branch of mathematics we know as trigonometry. He acquired a great deal of mathematical knowledge, including all the current work of the Egyptians and, indirectly, the Babylonians.

Thales was the first to use the idea of proof in geometry – pointing the way to abstract thinking. He helped to lay the foundations of geometry by demonstrating these five propositions:

- A circle is bisected by its diameter.
- In an isosceles triangle, the two angles opposite the equal sides are equal.
- Two pairs of parallel straight lines crossing each other form four angles and those opposite each other are equal.
- Any angle inscribed in a semi-circle is a right-angle.
- Two triangles are congruent if one has two angles and a side equal to two angles and a side of the other triangle.

The writing of proofs became an art – to be as concise as possible with the steps in reasoning, yet leaving no loopholes.

John Venn (1834 – 1923)

John Venn, an Englishman, wrote a textbook entitled *Symbolic Logic* which was published in 1881. After graduating from Cambridge in 1857, Venn spent some time as a parish priest, then in 1862 became a lecturer in moral science at his old university. He finally resigned from the priesthood in 1883 to devote all his time to studying and teaching logic. His earlier texts *The Logic of Chance* (1866) and *Symbolic Logic* (1881), were quickly followed by *Principles of Empirical Logic* (1889). All were quickly adopted as standard works in this field.

John Von Neumann (1903 – 1957)

Von Neumann contributed a great deal to the relatively new field of mathematics called *game theory*. This is a theory concerned with the mathematical way of describing and analyzing competition among groups of people (such as clubs, athletes, etc.), then recommending decisions or moves that should be made to 'win' in the competitive situation. He was fascinated by situations where strategy and chance play an important part, such as economics, science and military strategy.

Born in Budapest, Hungary, von Neumann had mastered college calculus by the age of eight and when only twenty three, he wrote a book called *Mathematical Foundations of Quantum Mechanics* (quantum mechanics was used in developing atomic energy).

From 1930 onwards, while in the United States, he became interested in the use of large-scale computers. This led him to build one if the first modern electronic brains, called MANIAC (Mathematical Analyzer, Numerical Integrator and Computer). In World War Two he designed nuclear weapons and missiles.

SOLUTIONS

Odd Numbers
14 = 11 + 1 + 1 + 1

Fibonacci Puzzle
No

Palindromic Numbers
1991

Dates :	09 – 1 – 90	19 – 1 – 91	29 – 1 – 92
	– 2 –	– 2 –	– 2 –
	– 3 –	– 3 –	– 3 –
	– 4 –	– 4 –	– 4 –
	– 5 –	– 5 –	– 5 –
	– 6 –	– 6 –	– 6 –
	– 7 –	– 7 –	– 7 –
	– 8 –	– 8 –	– 8 –
	– 9 –	– 9 –	– 9 –
	– 11 –	– 11 –	– 11 –

Total : 30

Times :

12.21

1.01	2.02	3.03	4.04	5.05	6.06	7.07	8.08	9.09	10.01
1.11	2.12	3.13	4.14	5.15	6.16	7.17	8.18	9.19	11.11
1.21	2.22	3.23	4.24	5.25	6.26	7.27	8.28	9.29	
1.31	2.32	3.33	4.34	5.35	6.36	7.37	8.38	9.39	
1.41	2.42	3.43	4.44	5.45	6.46	7.47	8.48	9.49	
1.51	2.52	3.53	4.54	5.55	6.56	7.57	8.58	9.59	

Total : 57 palindromic times

Calculator Capers
(b)   BASES 915 200
      GAINS 973 440
      SPEED 979 616
      MODERN 994 593
      GRIME
      FILES
      TORQUE ⎫ 997 920
      FORGE ⎬
      TULIPS ⎭
      GLASSY 998 400
      HEYDAY ⎫
      SHEND ⎬ 999 856
      HAWED ⎭

(d) 8, 12, 5 and 20   total 45

Zapping
There are 10 happy numbers between 10 and 50 inclusive. They are 10, 11, 13, 19, 23, 28, 31, 32, 44 and 49.

Beehive Cell Problems

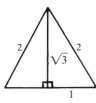

If P = 6
then A $= \frac{1}{2}$b.h
$= \frac{1}{2}.2.\sqrt{3}$
$= \sqrt{3}$
≈ 1.732

If P = 6
then A $= s^2$
$= (1\frac{1}{2})^2$
$= 2.25$

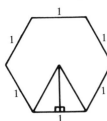

If P = 6
then A $= \frac{1}{2}$bh$\times$ 6
$= \frac{1}{2}.1.\frac{\sqrt{3}}{2}.6^3$
$= \frac{3\sqrt{3}}{2}$
≈ 2.59807

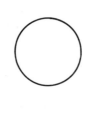

If P = 6
then $2\pi r = 6$
$\therefore r = \dfrac{6}{2\pi}$

Now A $= \pi r^2$
$= \pi.\dfrac{6^3}{2\pi}.\dfrac{6^3}{2\pi}$
$= \dfrac{9}{\pi}$
≈ 2.86

$\therefore$ hexagons have greatest area of the polygons.
(Circles do not tessellate.)

Cube Images
8, 11, 13, 12, 14, 22, 24, 21, 20, 37, 26, 38

Puzzle Corner
Area of hexagon is $3\sqrt{3}$ units^2

Tantalising Triangles

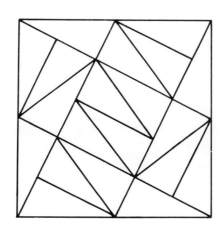

Dice Diversions

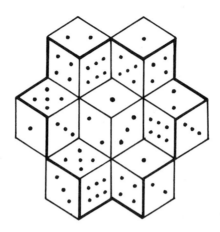

Decoding

My definition of a circle is a round straight line with a hole in the middle joined up so you can't see where it begins.

A googol is one followed by one hundred noughts. Write it in your book.

Lines by a Mystery Poet

A clever young student named Tom,
Made a miniature nuclear bomb,
When he pulled out the pin,
There came a great din,
And St Peter said, 'Where are you from?'.

Crossnumber with a Difference

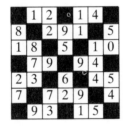

Combinations

2471 is the correct combination

Dissections

1.

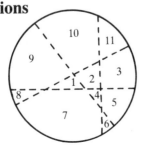

2.

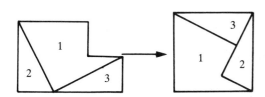

3. (a)

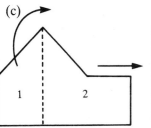

(b)

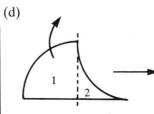

(c)

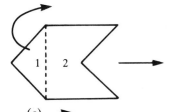

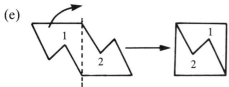

(d)

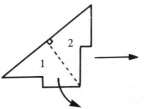

(e)

(f)

Octagon Transformation

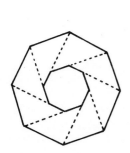

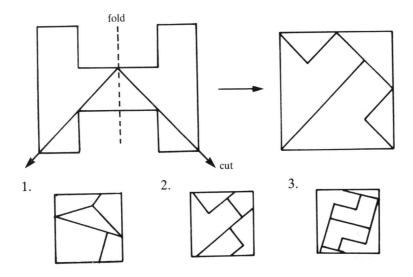

To Sharpen Your Wits

2.   Almost 300 years
4.   8.10 p.m.
5.   *This solution may be done by algebra, but can also be obtained by general reasoning.*
     In every hour the minute hand gains 55 minutes on the other hand i.e. in every minute it

     gains $\dfrac{55}{60}\left(\dfrac{11}{12}\right)$ of a minute, on the other hand.

     At 3 o'clock, the minute hand still has to gain 15 minutes on the hour hand and the
     time taken to do this will be:

$$15 \div \dfrac{11}{12} \text{ mins} = \dfrac{180}{11} \text{ mins}$$

$$= 16\dfrac{4}{11} \text{ mins}$$

i.e. $16\dfrac{4}{11}$ minutes after 3 o'clock.

Each answer obtained is a multiple of $5\dfrac{5}{11}$ minutes past the hour i.e. $1.05\dfrac{5}{11}$, $2.10\dfrac{10}{11}$, $3.16\dfrac{4}{11}$ etc.

Teasers

1.   2 apples
2.   9 sheep
3.   O

          O O

     O   O   O
4.   On the vertices of a tetrahedron.
5.   O   O O   O O O

         O O O   or   OOO

      O O   O   O O O

142

6.

Top coin is placed on corner one.

7. Myself: the second child is my sister.

8.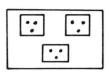

9. 50

10. 53 and 3

12.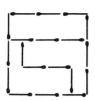

13.

14.

15.

16. 1961/1691
17. 24 white, 19 red, 12 green, 11 blue
18.

19. 5 cm (the shortest burns at the rate of 1 cm per hour). The others are 10 cm, 15 cm and 20 cm respectively.

20.

Mr Carpenter	Mr Baker	Mr Mason
Baker St	Mason St	Carpenter St
mason	carpenter	baker

21. John (doctor) ↔ Jane (artist)
    Peter (novelist) ↔ Robyn (secretary)
    Brian (pilot) ↔ Helen (singer)
23. Debbie is 12 years old. The others are: Diane 16, Denise 14, Deidre 10 and Donna 8.
24. The largest square is 8 cm
25. Deny
26. 1.39
     4.76
     2.58
    ―――
     8.73

27.

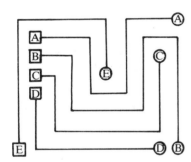

28. The remaining solid is an octahedron.
29. $123 - 4 - 5 - 6 - 7 + 8 - 9$ or
    $123 - 45 - 67 + 89$
30. $888 + 88 + 8 + 8 + 8$
31. The paradox is that he does shave himself *only if he does not* !

32.

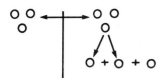

		8		10		
17	7	9		4	14	15
		3	19	11		
5	16	12		2	18	13
		1		6		

33. 59 minutes
34. 3 weighings

35. 10 people (and 12 dogs)
36. (a) by $\frac{3}{4}$
    (b) by $\frac{31}{32}$
37. Elizabeth weighs 36 kg
    Ann weighs 44 kg
    Carol weighs 20 kg
    David weighs 40 kg
    Mark weighs 30 kg
38. Let a stand for (1234567890)
    $\therefore$ the equation will be :
    $a^2 - (a - 1)(a + 1) = 1$ that reduces to $1 = 1$.
39. Area is approximately 3192 m^2 (side $\approx$ 56.5 m)
40. Triangle must have angles of 36°, 72° and 72° or 45°, 45° and 90°.
41. Joseph stood in the 31st position.
42. The secret is for you to make each pair of lines add to 99 999. Then count the number of pairs of lines (3 in the given example): so you multiply $3 \times 99\,999$ and write the answer 299 997.
43. 58 is the smallest one possible.

INDEX